Glencoe Mathematics

# Pre-Algebra

## Chapter 10
## Resource Masters

Glencoe

New York, New York   Columbus, Ohio   Chicago, Illinois   Peoria, Illinois   Woodland Hills, California

**Consumable Workbooks** Many of the worksheets contained in the Chapter Resource Masters are available as consumable workbooks in both English and Spanish.

| | ISBN10 | ISBN13 |
|---|---|---|
| Study Guide and Intervention Workbook | 0-07-877224-1 | 978-0-07-877224-6 |
| Skills Practice Workbook | 0-07-877216-8 | 978-0-07-877216-0 |
| Practice Workbook | 0-07-877218-4 | 978-0-07-877218-4 |
| Word Problem Practice Workbook | 0-07-877220-6 | 978-0-07-877220-7 |

## Spanish Versions

| | | |
|---|---|---|
| Study Guide and Intervention Workbook | 0-07-877224-1 | 978-0-07-877224-6 |
| Skills Practice Workbook | 0-07-877217-6 | 978-0-07-877217-7 |
| Practice Workbook | 0-07-877219-2 | 978-0-07-877219-1 |
| Word Problem Practice Workbook | 0-07-877221-4 | 978-0-07-877221-4 |

**Answers for Workbooks** The answers for Chapter 10 of these workbooks can be found in the back of this Chapter Resource Masters booklet.

**StudentWorks Plus™** This CD-ROM includes the entire Student Edition test along with the English workbooks listed above.

**TeacherWorks Plus™** All of the materials found in this booklet are included for viewing, printing, and editing in this CD-ROM.

**Spanish Assessment Masters** (ISBN10: 0-07-877222-2, ISBN13: 978-0-07-877222-1) These masters contain a Spanish version of Chapter 10 Test Form 2A and Form 2C.

 **Glencoe**

*The McGraw·Hill Companies*

Send all inquiries to:
Glencoe/McGraw-Hill
8787 Orion Place
Columbus, OH 43240

ISBN13: 978-0-07-873940-8
ISBN10: 0-07-873940-3

Printed in the United States of America.

2 3 4 5 6 7 8 9 10 024 13 12 11 10 09 08 07

# Contents

# Teacher's Guide to Using the Chapter 10 Resource Masters

The *Chapter 10 Resource Masters* includes the core materials needed for Chapter 10. These materials include worksheets, extensions, and assessment options. The answers for these pages appear at the back of this booklet.

All of the materials found in this booklet are included for viewing and printing in the *TeacherWorks Plus*™ CD-ROM.

## Chapter Resources

***Student-Built Glossary*** (pages 1–2) These masters are a student study tool that presents up to twenty of the key vocabulary terms from the chapter. Students are to record definitions and/or examples for each term. You may suggest that students highlight or star the terms with which they are not familiar. Give this to students before beginning Lesson 10-1. Encourage them to add these pages to their mathematics study notebooks. Remind them to complete the appropriate words as they study each lesson.

***Anticipation Guide*** (pages 3–4) This master, presented in both English and Spanish, is a survey used before beginning the chapter to pinpoint what students may or may not know about the concepts in the chapter. Students will revisit this survey after they complete the chapter to see if their perceptions have changed.

## Lesson Resources

***Lesson Reading Guide*** Get Ready for the Lesson extends the discussion from the beginning of the Student Edition lesson. Read the Lesson asks students to interpret the context of and relationships among terms in the lesson. Finally, Remember What You Learned asks students to summarize what they have learned using various representation techniques. Use as a study tool for note taking or as an informal reading assignment. It is also a helpful tool for ELL (English Language Learners).

***Study Guide and Intervention*** This master provides vocabulary, key concepts, additional worked-out examples and Check Your Progress exercises to use as a reteaching activity. It can also be used in conjunction with the Student Edition as an instructional tool for students who have been absent.

***Skills Practice*** This master focuses more on the computational nature of the lesson. Use as an additional practice option or as homework for second-day teaching of the lesson.

***Practice*** This master closely follows the types of problems found in the Exercises section of the Student Edition and includes word problems. Use as an additional practice option or as homework for second-day teaching of the lesson.

***Word Problem Practice*** This master includes additional practice in solving word problems that apply the concepts of the lesson. Use as an additional practice or as homework for second-day teaching of the lesson.

***Enrichment*** These activities may extend the concepts of the lesson, offer a historical or multicultural look at the concepts, or widen students' perspectives on the mathematics they are learning. They are written for use with all levels of students.

### Graphing Calculator, Scientific Calculator, or Spreadsheet Activities

These activities present ways in which technology can be used with the concepts in some lessons of this chapter. Use as an alternative approach to some concepts or as an integral part of your lesson presentation.

## Assessment Options

The assessment masters in the *Chapter 10 Resource Masters* offer a wide range of assessment tools for formative (monitoring) assessment and summative (final) assessment.

**Student Recording Sheet** This master corresponds with the standardized test practice at the end of the chapter.

**Pre-AP Rubric** This master provides information for teachers and students on how to assess performance on open-ended questions.

**Quizzes** Four free-response quizzes offer assessment at appropriate intervals in the chapter.

**Mid-Chapter Test** This 1-page test provides an option to assess the first half of the chapter. It parallels the timing of the Mid-Chapter Quiz in the Student Edition and includes both multiple-choice and free-response questions.

**Vocabulary Test** This test is suitable for all students. It includes a list of vocabulary words and 10 questions to assess students' knowledge of those words. This can also be used in conjunction with one of the leveled chapter tests.

### Leveled Chapter Tests

- *Form 1* contains multiple-choice questions and is intended for use with below grade level students.
- *Forms 2A and 2B* contain multiple-choice questions aimed at on grade level students. These tests are similar in format to offer comparable testing situations.
- *Forms 2C and 2D* contain free-response questions aimed at on grade level students. These tests are similar in format to offer comparable testing situations.
- *Form 3* is a free-response test for use with above grade level students.

All of the above tests include a free-response Bonus question.

**Extended-Response Test** Performance assessment tasks are suitable for all students. Sample answers and a scoring rubric are included for evaluation.

**Standardized Test Practice** These three pages are cumulative in nature. It includes three parts: multiple-choice questions with bubble-in answer format, griddable questions with answer grids, and short-answer free-response questions.

## Answers

- The answers for the Anticipation Guide and Lesson Resources are provided as reduced pages with answers appearing in red.
- Full-size answer keys are provided for the assessment masters.

# 10 Student-Built Glossary

Chapter Resources

This is an alphabetical list of key vocabulary terms you will learn in Chapter 10. As you study this chapter, complete each term's definition or description. Remember to add the page number where you found the term. Add these pages to your Pre-Algebra Study Notebook to review vocabulary at the end of the chapter.

| Vocabulary Term | Found on Page | Definition/Description/Example |
|---|---|---|
| adjacent (uh-JAY-suhnt) angles | | |
| alternate exterior angles | | |
| alternate interior angles | | |
| altitude | | |
| base | | |
| circle | | |
| circumference<br>suhr-KUHMP-fuhrnts | | |
| complementary<br>kahm-pluh-MEHN-tuh-ree | | |
| composite figures | | |
| congruent<br>kuhn-GROO-uhnt | | |
| corresponding angles | | |
| diameter | | |

# 10 Student-Built Glossary *(continued)*

| Vocabulary Term | Found on Page | Definition/Description/Example |
|---|---|---|
| dilation | | |
| parallel lines | | |
| parallelogram | | |
| perpendicular lines | | |
| quadrilateral<br>KWAH-druh-LA-tuh-ruhl | | |
| radius | | |
| reflection | | |
| regular polygon | | |
| rhombus | | |
| supplementary<br>SUH-pluh-MEHN-tuh-ree | | |
| transformation | | |
| translation | | |
| transversal | | |
| vertical angles | | |

# 10 Anticipation Guide

## Measuring Two-Dimensional Figures

**Step 1** *Before you begin Chapter 10*

• Read each statement.

• Decide whether you Agree (A) or Disagree (D) with the statement.

• Write A or D in the first column OR if you are not sure whether you agree or disagree, write NS (Not Sure).

| STEP 1 A, D, or NS | Statement | Step 2 A or D |
|---|---|---|
| | 1. Parallel lines intersect in only one point. | |
| | 2. When two parallel lines are intersected by a third line, eight angles are formed. | |
| | 3. If the sum of the measures of two angles is 180°, the angles are complimentary. | |
| | 4. Any two lines that intersect to form a right angle are perpendicular lines. | |
| | 5. Two figures are congruent if they have the same size and shape. | |
| | 6. To graph the ordered pair (3, 5) on coordinate plane, start at the origin and move three units up, then move five units to the right. | |
| | 7. A quadrilateral is a closed figure with five sides. | |
| | 8. If both pairs of opposite sides of a quadrilateral are parallel, then the quadrilateral is a parallelogram. | |
| | 9. The area of a figure is the surface enclosed by that figure. | |
| | 10. A trapezoid has two pairs of parallel sides. | |
| | 11. All triangles are polygons. | |
| | 12. The diameter of a circle is the distance from the center to any point on the circle. | |

**Step 2** *After you complete Chapter 10*

• Reread each statement and complete the last column by entering an A (Agree) or a D (Disagree).

• Did any of your opinions about the statements change from the first column?

• For those statements that you mark with a D, use a separate sheet of paper to explain why you disagree. Use examples, if possible.

## 10 Ejercicios preparatorios

### Mide figuras bidimensionales

**Paso 1** *Antes de comenzar el Capítulo 10*

- Lee cada enunciado.
- Decide si estás de acuerdo (A) o en desacuerdo (D) con el enunciado.
- Escribe A o D en la primera columna O si no estás seguro(a) de la respuesta, escribe NS (No estoy seguro(a)).

| PASO 1<br>A, D o NS | Enunciado | PASO 2<br>A o D |
|---|---|---|
| | **1.** Las rectas paralelas se intersecan en un punto solamente. | |
| | **2.** Cuando una tercera recta interseca a dos rectas paralelas, se forman ocho ángulos. | |
| | **3.** Si la suma de las medidas de dos ángulos es 180°, los ángulos son complementarios. | |
| | **4.** Dos rectas cualesquiera que se intersecan para formar un ángulo recto son rectas perpendiculares. | |
| | **5.** Dos figuras son congruentes si tienen la misma forma y tamaño. | |
| | **6.** Para graficar el par ordenado (3, 5) en un plano de coordenadas, se comienza en el origen y se mueve tres unidades hacia arriba y luego cinco unidades hacia la derecha. | |
| | **7.** Un cuadrilátero es una figura cerrada con cinco lados. | |
| | **8.** Si ambos pares de lados opuestos de un cuadrilátero son paralelos, entonces el cuadrilátero es un paralelogramo. | |
| | **9.** El área de una figura es la superficie ocupada por ella. | |
| | **10.** Un trapecio tiene dos pares de lados paralelos. | |
| | **11.** Todos los triángulos son polígonos. | |
| | **12.** El diámetro de un círculo es la distancia desde el centro hasta cualquier punto en la circunferencia. | |

**Paso 2** *Después de completar el Capítulo 10*

- Vuelve a leer cada enunciado y completa la última columna con una A o una D.
- ¿Cambió cualquiera de tus opiniones sobre los enunciados de la primera columna?
- En una hoja de papel aparte, escribe un ejemplo de por qué estás en desacuerdo con los enunciados que marcaste con una D.

# 10-1 Lesson Reading Guide

## Line and Angle Relationships

## Get Ready for the Lesson

**Read the introduction to Lesson 10-1 in your textbook. Write your answers below.**

**a.** What do you notice about the lines coming into the satellite dish?

**b.** Trace the red lines onto a piece of paper. Find the measure of each angle.

**c.** What do you notice about the measures of the angles? Which angles have the same measure?

## Read the Lesson

**Write a definition and give an example of each new vocabulary word or phrase.**

| Vocabulary | Definition | Example |
|---|---|---|
| **1.** parallel lines | | |
| **2.** interior angles | | |
| **3.** exterior angles | | |
| **4.** corresponding angles | | |
| **5.** vertical angles | | |
| **6.** adjacent angles | | |
| **7.** complementary angles | | |
| **8.** supplementary angles | | |

## Remember What You Learned

**9.** Draw two parallel, horizontal lines. Draw a third line (transversal) so it intersects the first pair. Label the eight angles. Identify two interior angles. (Interior angles are between the parallel lines.) Identify three angles that have the same measure. (Opposite and corresponding angles have the same measure.) If two angles are supplementary, and one of the angles measures 50°, what must the other angle measure? (Supplementary angles always equal 180°.)

## 10-1 Study Guide and Intervention

### Line and Angle Relationships

| Names of Special Angles | | |
|---|---|---|
| **Interior angles** lie inside the parallel lines. | $\angle 3, \angle 4, \angle 5, \angle 6$ | 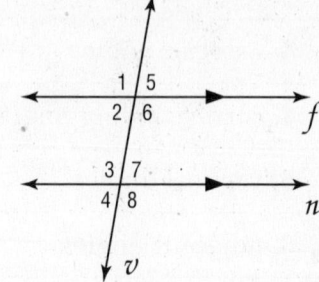 |
| **Exterior angles** lie outside the parallel lines. | $\angle 1, \angle 2, \angle 7, \angle 8$ | |
| **Alternate interior angles** are on opposite sides of the transversal and inside the parallel lines. | $\angle 3$, and $\angle 5$, $\angle 4$ and $\angle 6$ | |
| **Alternate exterior angles** are on opposite sides of the transversal and outside the parallel lines. | $\angle 1$ and $\angle 7$, $\angle 2$, and $\angle 8$ | |
| **Corresponding angles** are in the same position on the parallel lines in relation to the transversal. | $\angle 1$ and $\angle 5$, $\angle 2$ and $\angle 6$, $\angle 3$ and $\angle 7$, $\angle 4$ and $\angle 8$ | |

| Line and Angle Relationships | | | | | |
|---|---|---|---|---|---|
| **Parallel Lines** | **Perpendicular Lines** | **Vertical Angles** | **Adjacent Angles** | **Compelementary Angles** | **Supplementary Angles** |
| $a \parallel b$ | $m \perp n$ | $\angle 1 \cong \angle 3$ $\angle 2 \cong \angle 4$ | $m\angle ABC = m\angle 1 + m\angle 2$ | $m\angle 1 + m\angle 2 = 90°$ | $m\angle 1 + m\angle 2 = 180°$ |

**Example**  In the figure, $f \parallel n$ and $v$ is a transversal. If $m\angle 3 = 100°$, find $m\angle 1$ and $m\angle 6$.

Since $\angle 1$ and $\angle 3$ are corresponding angles, they are congruent. So, $m\angle 1 = 100°$. Since $\angle 3$ and $\angle 6$ are alternate interior angles, they are congruent. So, $m\angle 6 = 100°$.

**Exercises**

Find the value of $x$ in each figure.

1. 150° $x°$

2. 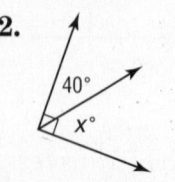 40° $x°$

3. 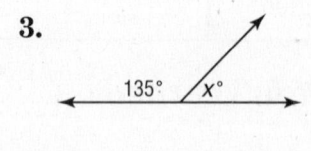 135° $x°$

4. 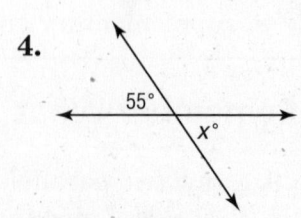 55° $x°$

5. **ALGEBRA** Angles $A$ and $B$ are complementary. If $m\angle A = 3x - 8$ and $m\angle B = 5x + 10$, what is the measure of each angle?

6. **ALGEBRA** Angles $Q$ and $R$ are supplementary. If $m\angle Q = 4x + 9$ and $m\angle R = 8x + 3$, what is the measure of each angle?

## 10-1 Skills Practice

### Line and Angle Relationships

In the figure at the right, $c \parallel d$ and $p$ is a transversal.
If $m\angle 5 = 110°$, find the measure of each angle.

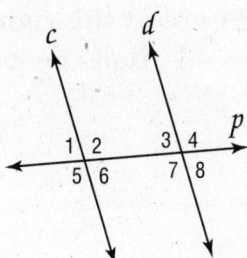

1. $\angle 6$

2. $\angle 8$

3. $\angle 2$

4. $\angle 4$

In the figure at the right, $g \parallel k$ and $r$ is a transversal.
If $m\angle 7 = 60°$, find the measure of each angle.

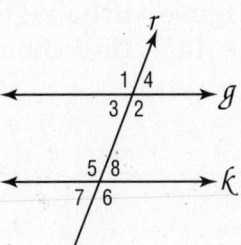

5. $\angle 4$

6. $\angle 6$

7. $\angle 5$

8. $\angle 3$

Find the value of $x$ in each figure.

9.

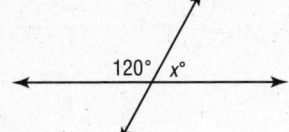

10.

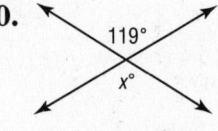

11.

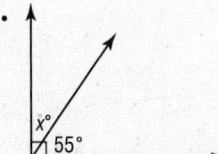

12.

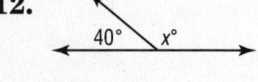

13.

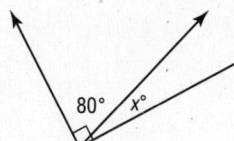

14.

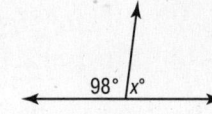

15.

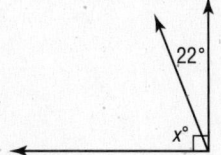

16.

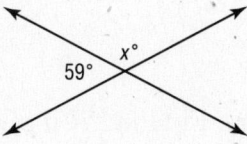

17.

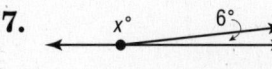

18.

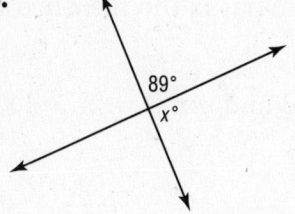

19.

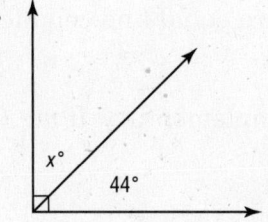

20.

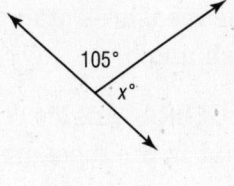

**Practice**

## Line and Angle Relationships

In the figure at the right, $m \parallel n$ and $r$ is a transversal.
If $m\angle 2 = 45°$, find the measure of each angle.

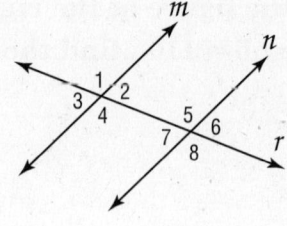

1. $\angle 4$                    2. $\angle 5$

3. $\angle 7$                    4. $\angle 8$

5. $\angle 6$                    6. $\angle 3$

In the figure at the right, $d \parallel e$ and $a$ is a transversal.
If $m\angle 5 = 143°$, find the measure of each angle.

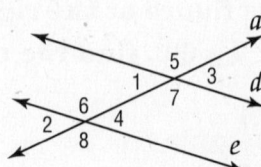

7. $\angle 7$                    8. $\angle 6$

9. $\angle 4$                    10. $\angle 2$

11. $\angle 1$                   12. $\angle 8$

Find the value of $x$ in each figure.

13.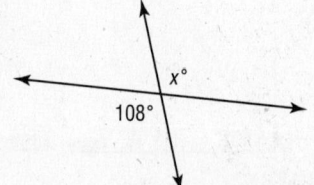

14.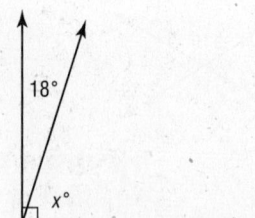

15.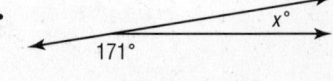

16.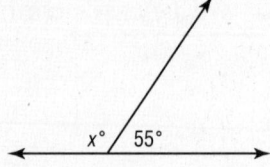

17.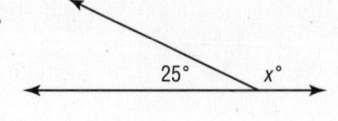

18.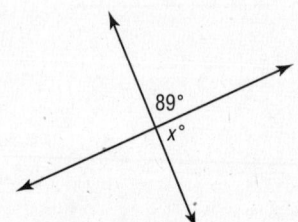

19. Angles $Q$ and $R$ are complementary. Find $m\angle R$ if $m\angle Q = 24°$.

20. Find $m\angle J$ if $m\angle K = 29°$ and $\angle J$ and $\angle K$ are supplementary.

21. The measures of angles $A$ and $B$ are equal and complementary. What is the measure of each angle?

22. **ALGEBRA** Angles $G$ and $H$ are complementary. If $m\angle G = 3x + 6$ and $m\angle H = 2x - 11$, what is the measure of each angle?

## 10-1  Word Problem Practice

### Line and Angle Relationships

1. **PROPERTY LINES** The front and back property lines of Michaela's land are parallel lines. If the angle between the west side property line and back property line is 106°, what is the angle between the front property line and west side property line?

2. **SCISSORS** Archie opened up a pair of scissor so that the angle between the blades is 38°. What is the angle between the handles?

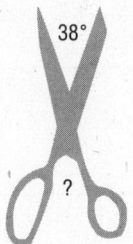

3. **FENCING** The sections of fence in Sioban's yard have diagonal supports as shown. The top side of the diagonal support makes an angle of $x°$ with the fence slats. The bottom side makes an angle that is twice the measure of the top angle. Find the measures of both angles.

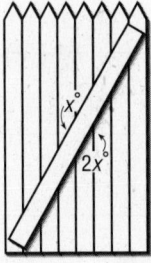

4. **MAPS** In the following map, First Avenue, Second Avenue, and Third Avenue are parallel. Cross Street intersects all three avenues. First Avenue and Cross Street meet at a 25° angle. What angle does the intersection of Third Avenue and Cross Street make?

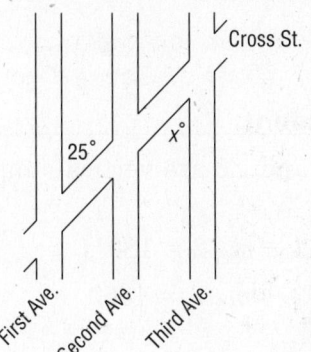

**HIKING  For Exercises 5 and 6, use the following information.**

Dave and Susie are walking on parallel trails in the woods. Dave's trail turns to the right 43° and meets up with Susie's trail.

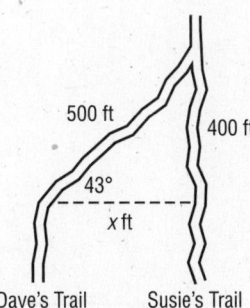

5. At what angle does Dave's trail meet Susie's trail?

6. How far apart were Dave and Susie's trails originally?

## 10-1  Enrichment

## *Geometric Proof*

Use definitions and theorems for angle congruence to complete the proofs.

**Write the reason for each statement.**

**1. Prove:** $\angle 1 \cong \angle 3$

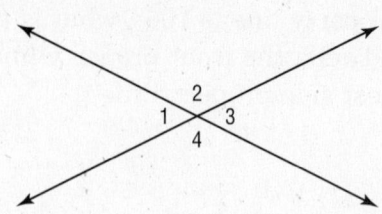

| Statement | Reason |
|---|---|
| **a.** $\angle 1$ and $\angle 3$ are vertical angles. | **a.** Given |
| **b.** $m\angle 1 + m\angle 2 = 180°$; $m\angle 3 + m\angle 2 = 180°$ | **b.** _____ |
| **c.** $m\angle 1 = 180° - m\angle 2$; $m\angle 3 = 180° - m\angle 2$ | **c.** _____ |
| **d.** $m\angle 1 = m\angle 3$ | **d.** _____ |
| **e.** $\angle 1 \cong \angle 3$ | **e.** _____ |

**2. Prove:** $m\angle 3 \cong m\angle 7$

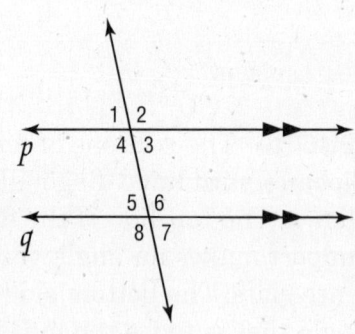

| Statement | Reason |
|---|---|
| **a.** Line $p$ is parallel to line $q$. | **a.** Given |
| **b.** $m\angle 3 \cong m\angle 5$ | **b.** _____ |
| **c.** $m\angle 5 \cong m\angle 7$ | **c.** _____ |
| **d.** $m\angle 3 \cong m\angle 7$ | **d.** _____ |

# 10-2 Lesson Reading Guide

## *Congruent Triangles*

## Get Ready for the Lesson

**Read the introduction to Lesson 10-2 in your textbook. Write your answers below.**

**a.** Trace the triangles shown in your textbook onto a sheet of paper. Then label the triangles.

**b.** Measure and then compare the lengths of the sides of the triangles.

**c.** Measure the angles of each triangle. How do the angles compare?

**d.** Make a conjecture about the triangles.

## Read the Lesson

**Write a definition and give an example of each new vocabulary word or phrase.**

| Vocabulary | Definition | Example |
|---|---|---|
| **1.** congruent | | |
| **2.** corresponding parts | | |

## Remember What You Learned

**3.** Below are two congruent triangles. Name the corresponding parts and complete the congruence statement.

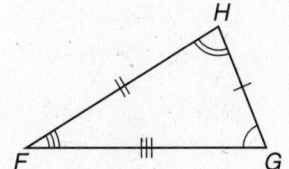   $\triangle GHF \cong$ ___?___

Lesson 10-2

# 10-2 Study Guide and Intervention

## Congruent Triangles

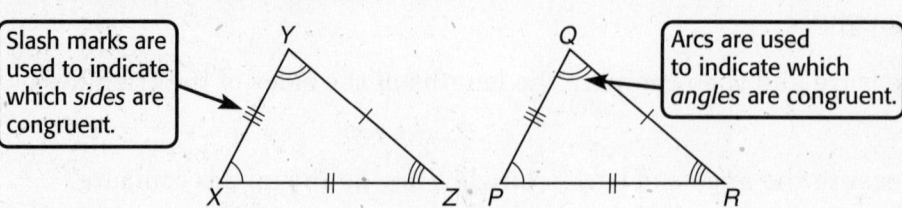

| Corresponding Parts of Congruent Triangles | |
|---|---|
| **Words** | Two triangles are **congruent** if they have the same size and shape. |
| | If two triangles are congruent, their corresponding sides are congruent and their corresponding angles are congruent. |
| **Model** | Slash marks are used to indicate which *sides* are congruent. Arcs are used to indicate which *angles* are congruent. |
| **Symbols** | Congruent Angles: $\angle X \cong \angle P$, $\angle Y \cong \angle Q$, $\angle Z \cong \angle R$ |
| | Congruent Sides: $\overline{XY} \cong \overline{PQ}$, $\overline{YZ} \cong \overline{QR}$, $\overline{XZ} \cong \overline{PR}$ |

**Example**  Name the corresponding parts in the congruent triangles shown. Then write a congruence statement.

Corresponding Angles

$\angle Q \cong \angle S$; $\angle R \cong \angle Z$, $\angle N \cong \angle V$

Corresponding Sides

$\overline{SZ} \cong \overline{QR}$, $\overline{ZV} \cong \overline{RN}$, $\overline{VS} \cong \overline{NQ}$

$\triangle NQR \cong \triangle VSZ$

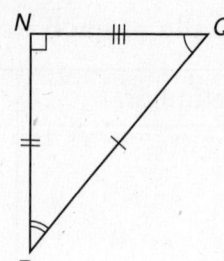
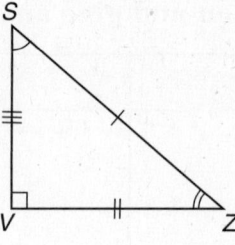

**Exercises**

Complete each congruence statement if $\triangle DFH \cong \triangle PWZ$.

**1.** $\angle F \cong$ _____

**2.** $\angle P \cong$ _____

**3.** $\overline{DH} \cong$ _____

**4.** $\overline{ZW} \cong$ _____

Find the value of $x$ for each pair of congruent triangles.

**5.**
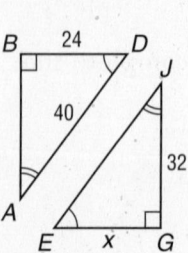

**6.**
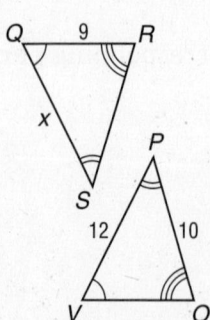

**7.**
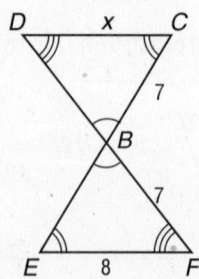

**8.**
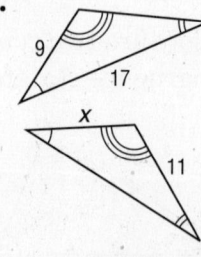

# 10-2 Skills Practice

## Congruent Triangles

For each pair of congruent triangles, name the corresponding parts. Then complete the congruence statement.

1.

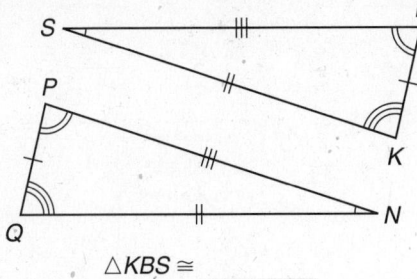

△KBS ≅ _____

2.

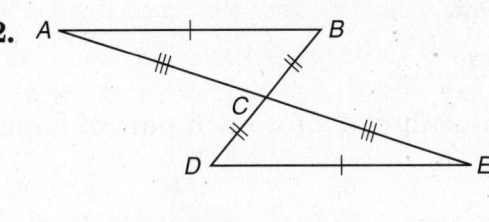

△ACB ≅ _____

Complete each congruence statement if △MRU ≅ △ACF.

3. ∠R ≅ ___?___    4. $\overline{CA}$ ≅ ___?___    5. MU ≅ ___?___    6. ∠A ≅ ___?___

Complete each congruence statement if △GLE ≅ △SPT.

7. $\overline{EL}$ ≅ ___?___    8. ∠S ≅ ___?___    9. ∠E ≅ ___?___    10. $\overline{PS}$ ≅ ___?___

Find the value of x for each pair of congruent triangles.

11.

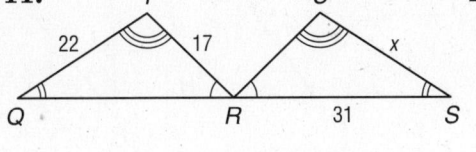

12.

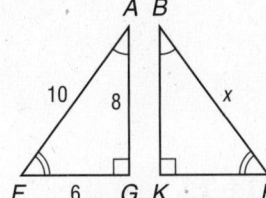

13.

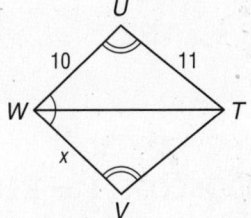

ARCHITECTURE  For Exercises 14 and 15, use the diagram of the Eiffel Tower truss at the right and the fact that △ACB ≅ △DFE.

14. Find the distance between A and B.

15. What is the measure of ∠B?

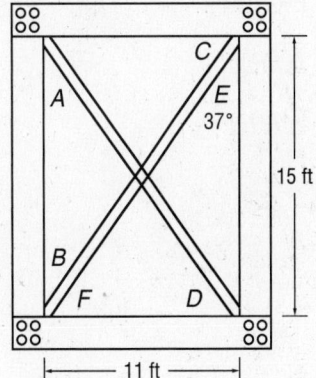

Lesson 10-2

# 10-2 Practice

## Congruent Triangles

**Complete the congruence statement if △CMH ≅ △PLF and △DNO ≅ △AET.**

1. ∠M ≅ ___?___

2. $\overline{MC}$ ≅ ___?___

3. $\overline{DN}$ ≅ ___?___

4. ∠A ≅ ___?___

5. $\overline{FL}$ ≅ ___?___

6. ∠C ≅ ___?___

7. $\overline{TE}$ ≅ ___?___

8. ∠O ≅ ___?___

**Find the value of x for each pair of congruent triangles.**

9.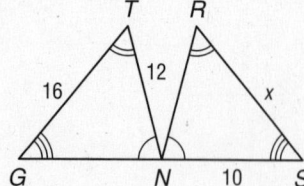

10.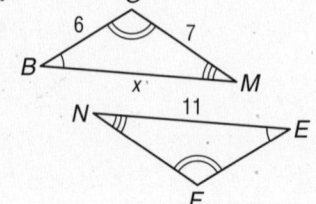

11.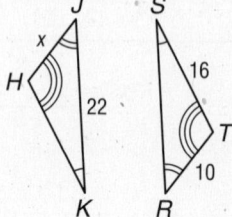

12. **ALGEBRA** If △DEC ≅ △PRM, what is the value of x?

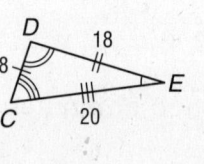
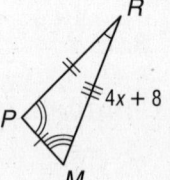

13. **ALGEBRA** If △AHB ≅ △KJP, what is the value of x?

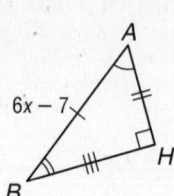
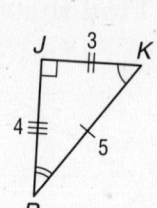

**KALEIDOSCOPE For Exercises 14–19, use the kaleidoscope pattern at the right. Name a triangle that appears to be congruent to each triangle listed.**

14. △GEH

15. △FCH

16. △DEC

17. △ABD

18. △HEF

19. △CBE

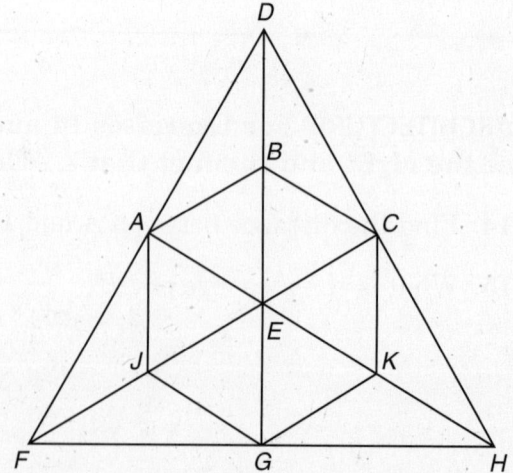

## 10-2 Word Problem Practice

### Congruent Triangles

**1. ROOFING** The structure of a roof can be broken into congruent triangles. If side $\overline{WX}$ is 12 feet long, what is the length of side $\overline{WZ}$?

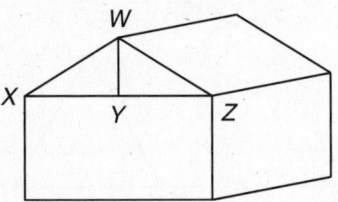

**2. CONSTRUCTION** Braces are often used to support walls during the construction of a house. If the two braces used in the following house are the same length and perpendicular to the ground, what is the measure of the angle $x$ where the braces meet the ground?

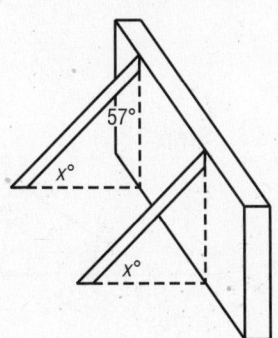

**3. FLOWER BEDS** Jane has two congruent flower beds in her backyard. The flower beds are triangular in shape. If the longest side of one flower bed is 12 feet, how long is the longest side of the other flower bed?

**4. AWARDS** The award for Most Improved Math Student in Mrs. Pike's classroom is a circle containing two congruent triangles connected at a vertex. What side in $\triangle ABC$ corresponds to $\overline{DE}$?

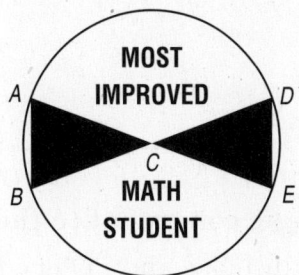

**KITES** For Exercises 5 and 6, use the following information.

Joey's kite is made up of 4 congruent right triangles and 1 square as shown in the diagram below.

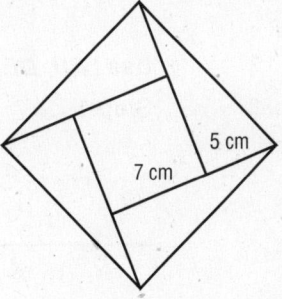

**5.** What are the three side lengths of each triangle?

**6.** What is the perimeter of Joey's kite?

Lesson 10-2

**10-2** **Enrichment**

## Constructions: Congruent Triangles

**Construct a triangle congruent to the given triangle using the SSS rule.**

(Three sides of one triangle are congruent to three sides of another triangle.)

Given △ ABC     Step 1         Step 2         Step 3

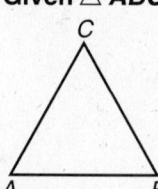 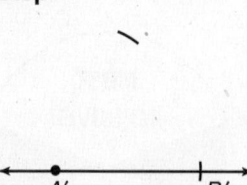 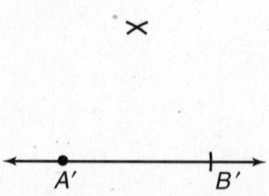 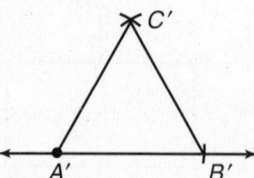

**Construct a triangle congruent to the given triangle using the SAS rule.**

(Two sides and the included angle of one triangle are congruent to two sides and the included angle of another triangle.)

Given △ RST    Use ($\overline{RT}$, ∠T, $\overline{ST}$).

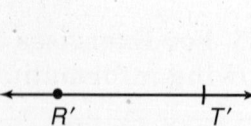 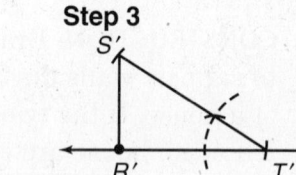

**Construct a triangle congruent to the given triangle using the ASA rule.**

(Two angles and the included side of one triangle are congruent to two angles and the included side of another triangle.)

Given △ DEF    Use (∠D, $\overline{DE}$, ∠E).

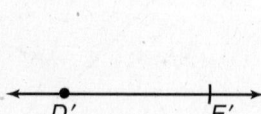 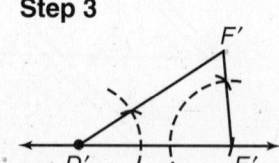

**Construct a triangle congruent to triangle *KJL*.
Use the rule and parts specified.**

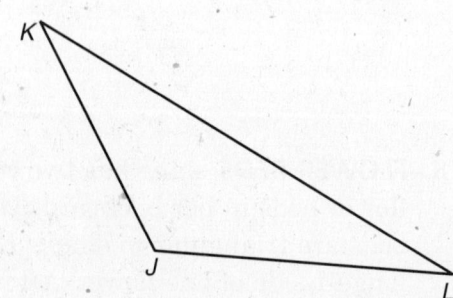

1. SSS; Use: $\overline{JL}$, $\overline{JK}$, $\overline{KL}$

2. SAS; Use: $\overline{JL}$, ∠L, $\overline{KL}$

3. ASA; Use: ∠K, $\overline{KL}$, ∠L

# 10-3 Lesson Reading Guide

## Transformations on the Coordinate Plane

### Get Ready for the Lesson

Read the introduction to Lesson 10-3 in your textbook. Write your answers below.

**a.** Describe the motion involved in making a 180° turn on a skateboard.

**b.** What type of motion does a scooter display when moving forward?

### Read the Lesson

Write a definition and give an example of each new vocabulary word or phrase.

| Vocabulary | Definition | Example |
|---|---|---|
| **1.** transformation | | |
| **2.** translation | | |
| **3.** reflection | | |
| **4.** line of symmetry | | |
| **5.** dilation | | |

### Remember What You Learned

**6.** Complete the diagrams below by filling in each blank with one of the vocabulary words or phrases.

A movement of a geometric figure is called a _____.

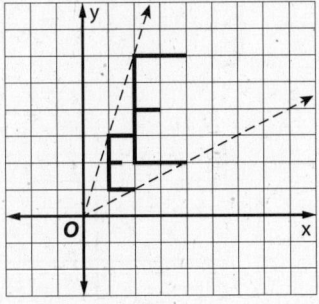 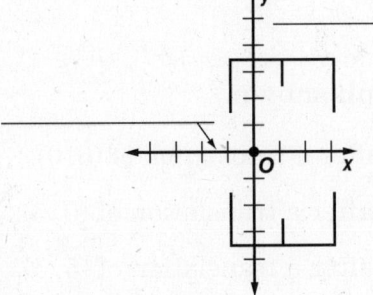 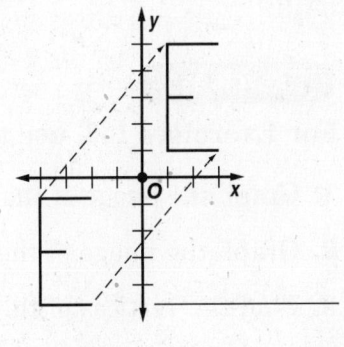

Lesson 10-3

# 10-3 Study Guide and Intervention

## Transformations on the Coordinate Plane

| Transformation | Movement | How To's |
|---|---|---|
| **Translation** | You slide a figure from one position to another without turning it. Every point of the original figure is moved the same distance and in the same direction. | To describe the translation using an ordered pair, add the coordinates of the ordered pair to the coordinates of the original point. |
| **Reflection** | You flip a figure over a **line of symmetry**. The figures are mirror images of each other. Every corresponding point on the figure after a reflection is called its **image.** | • To reflect a point over the *x*-axis, use the same *x*-coordinate and multiply the *y*-coordinate by −1.<br>• To reflect a point over the *y*-axis, use the same *y*-coordinate and multiply the *x*-coordinate by −1. |
| **Dilation** | You enlarge or reduce a figure by a scale factor with respect to a fixed point called the center. The resulting image is similar to the original figure. | • To dilate a figure when the center of dilation is the origin, multiply each coordinate by the scale factor.<br>• To dilate a figure for any other center of dilation is not the origin, subtract the coordinates for the center of dilation from the coordinates of each point, multiply by the scale factor, and then add the coordinates for the center of dilation. |

**Example**  The vertices of figure *PQRS* are $P(-2, 2)$, $Q(-1, 2)$, $R(-1, -2)$, and $S(-3, -1)$. Graph the figure and its image after a reflection over the *y*-axis. Use the same *y*-coordinate and multiply the *x*-coordinate by –1.

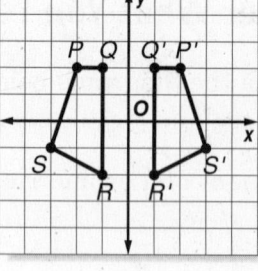

| vertex | | | | reflection |
|---|---|---|---|---|
| $P(-2, 2)$ | → | $(-2 \cdot -1, 2)$ | → | $P'(2, 2)$ |
| $Q(-1, 2)$ | → | $(-1 \cdot -1, 2)$ | → | $Q'(1, 2)$ |
| $R(-1, -2)$ | → | $(-1 \cdot -1, -2)$ | → | $R'(1, -2)$ |
| $S(-3, -1)$ | → | $(-3 \cdot -1, -1)$ | → | $S'(3, -1)$ |

**Exercises**

For Exercises 1–3, use the graph shown.

1. Graph the image of the figure after a translation of (5, 0).

2. Graph the image of the figure after a translation of (0, 5).

3. Find the vertices of the figure after a translation of (5, 5).

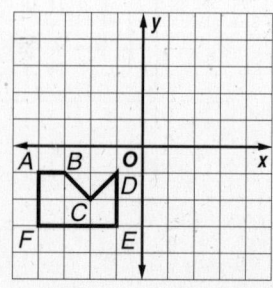

**18**

## 10-3 Skills Practice

### Transformations on the Coordinate Plane

**Find the coordinates of the vertices of each figure after the given translation. Then graph the translation image.**

**1.** (5, 2)

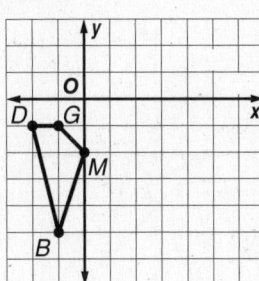

**2.** (−3, 4)

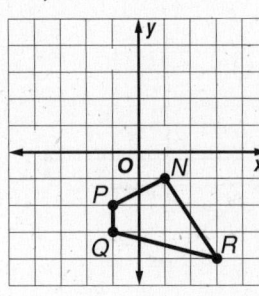

**3.** (−1, −5)

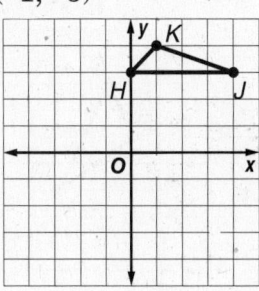

**Find the coordinates of the vertices of each figure after a reflection over the given axis. Then graph the reflection image.**

**4.** *y*-axis

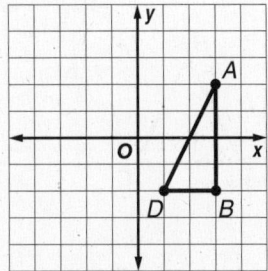

**5.** *x*-axis

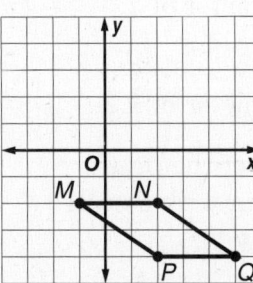

**6.** *x*-axis

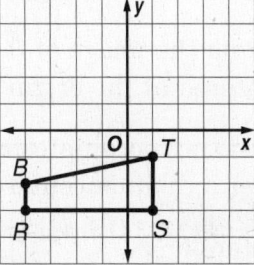

**For Exercises 7–8, use the graph shown.**

**7.** Graph the image of the figure after a dilation centered at the origin with a scale factor of 2.

**8.** Find the coordinates of the vertices after a dilation centered at the origin with a scale factor of $\frac{1}{2}$.

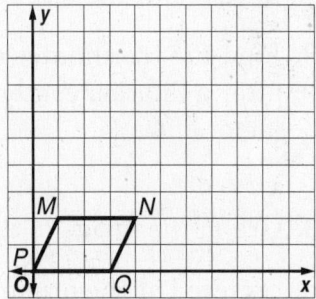

# 10-3 Practice

## Transformations on the Coordinate Plane

Find the coordinates of the vertices of each figure after a reflection over the given axis. Then graph the reflection image.

**1.** y–axis

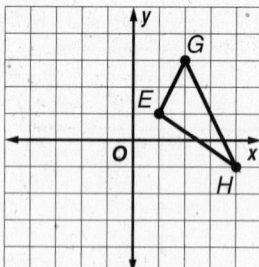

**2.** x–axis

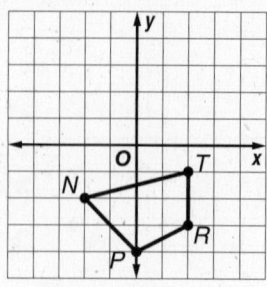

**3.** x–axis

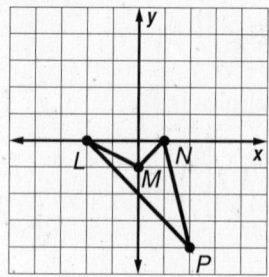

**For Exercises 4–6, use the graph shown.**

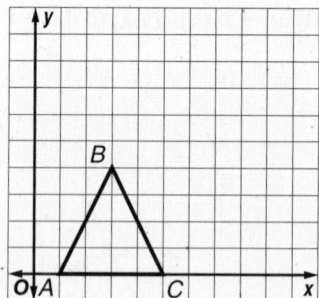

**4.** Graph the image of the figure after a dilation centered at the origin with a scale factor of 2.

**5.** Graph the image of the figure after a dilation centered at the origin with a scale factor of 1.5.

**6.** Find the coordinates of the vertices of the figure after a dilation centered at the origin with a scale factor of $\frac{1}{2}$.

**For Exercises 7–9, use the graph shown.**

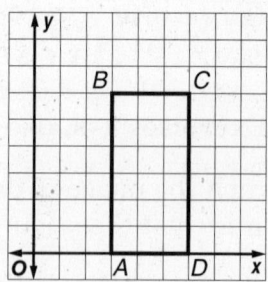

**7.** Graph the image of the figure after a dilation centered at the origin with a scale factor of $\frac{1}{3}$.

**8.** Find the coordinates of the vertices of the figure after a dilation centered at the origin with a scale factor of 4.

**9.** Graph the image of the figure after a dilation centered at the origin with a scale factor of $\frac{4}{3}$.

## 10-3 **Word Problem Practice**

### *Transformations on the Coordinate Plane*

1. **MAPPING** Francesca wants to rearrange her bedroom, so she drew the floor plan of her bedroom on a coordinate grid. If her bed was originally located in the second quadrant, which quadrant will it be in if she rotates its position 90° clockwise?

2. **ARCHEOLOGY** Archeologists use a grid to record the location of artifacts in a dig site. An assistant marked grid A3 as the location of two arrow heads. The arrowheads were actually found in the grid 4 units to the right and 3 units down. Which grid should the assistant record as the location of the arrowheads?

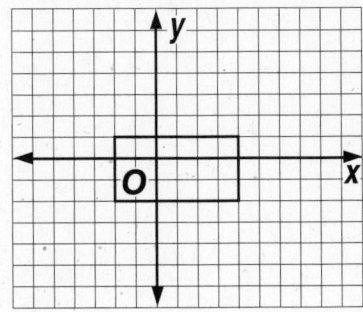

3. **SWIMMING POOLS** Mrs. Jensen is planning to have a swimming pool installed. The contractor drew the pool on the coordinate grid. Jenny wants a bigger pool and decides a dilation with scale factor 2 centered at the origin will be sufficient. What are the coordinate of the vertices of the new pool?

4. **GAMES** In the game of checkers, the pieces are set up in a particular order. Which transformation would place checker *A* on top of checker *B*?

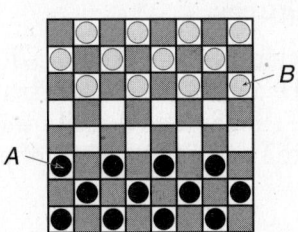

**MODELS** For Exercises 5 and 6, use the following information.

Long-grass Landscape Company often draws a scale model of yards they are designing. The scale factor of the model shown is 1 inch to 10 feet.

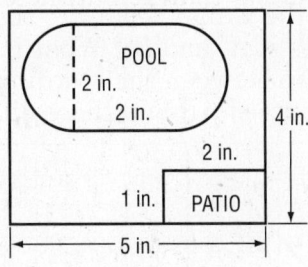

5. Does this model represent a dilation, translation, or reflection of the actual yard?

6. What will be the actual dimensions of the patio?

**Lesson 10-3**

## 10-3 **Enrichment**

### *Translations and Reflections*

**The lines on graph paper can help you draw slide images of figures.**

1. Graph $\triangle ABC$ with vertices $A(1, 1)$, $B(-3, 4)$, and $C(-3, -4)$. Draw $\triangle A'B'C'$, the translation image of $\triangle ABC$, where the slide is 3 units to the right. Name the coordinates of the image of each vertex.

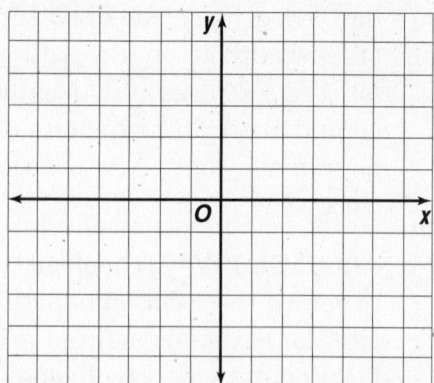

2. Draw $\triangle JKL$ with vertices $J(-4, 3)$, $K(0, 2)$, and $L(-2, 0)$. Let $\triangle J'K'L'$ be the image of $\triangle JKL$ under a slide of 4 units to the right and then a slide of 3 units up. Graph $\triangle J'K'L'$. Name the coordinates of the vertices of $\triangle J'K'L'$.

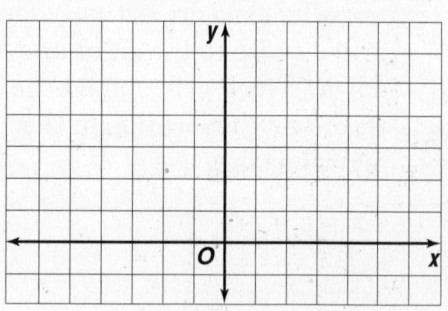

3. Draw $\overline{A'B'}$, the image formed by reflecting $\overline{AB}$ over the $y$-axis. Then draw $\overline{A''B''}$, the image formed by reflecting $\overline{A'B'}$ over the $x$-axis. What are the coordinates of $A''$ and $B''$? What is the relationship between the coordinates of the endpoints of $\overline{AB}$ and those of $\overline{A''B''}$?

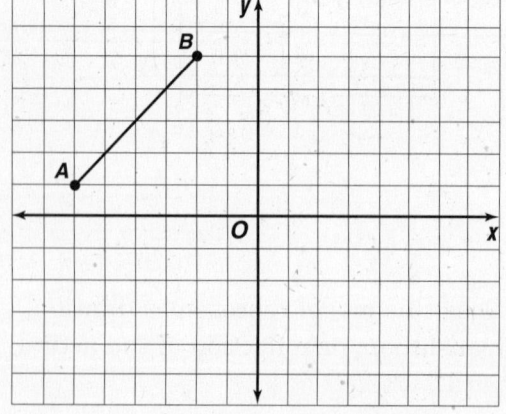

4. Draw $\overline{P'Q'}$, the reflection image of $\overline{PQ}$ over the $y$-axis. Draw $\overline{P''Q''}$, the reflection image of $\overline{P'Q'}$ over the $x$-axis. Find the slopes of $\overline{PQ}$, $\overline{P'Q'}$, and $\overline{P''Q''}$. What is the relationship between the slopes of $\overline{PQ}$ and $\overline{P''Q''}$?

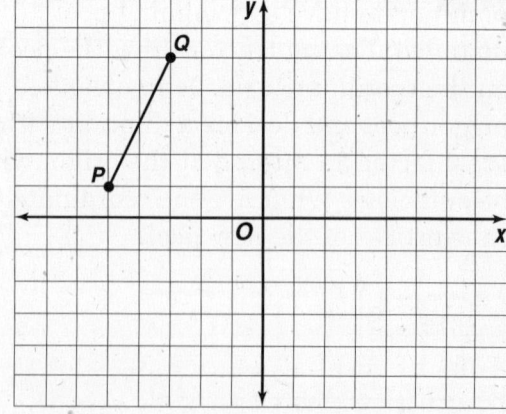

# 10-3 Graphing Calculator Activity

## Transformations

Transformations can be graphed by using lists and scatter plots. To review lists and scatter plots, see pages 39 to 42 of your Student Edition.

**Example 1** Graph △*ABC* with *A*(2, 1), *B*(4, 3), and *C*(6, 0). Then graph a triangle with a perimeter that is 3 times that of △*ABC*.

Enter the *x*-coordinates of the vertices in the **L1** list. Then enter the *y*-coordinates in **L2**. Repeat the coordinates of point *A* so that the scatter plot will form a closed figure. To graph △*ABC*, turn **Plot1** on and select the connected scatter plot (⌐△), and define the plot using **L1** and **L2**. Press [GRAPH].

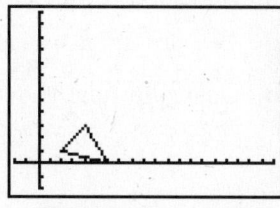

[−2, 20] scl:1 by [−2, 12] scl:1

Keystrokes: [STAT] [ENTER] 2 [ENTER] 4 [ENTER] 6 [ENTER] 2 [ENTER] [▶] 1 [ENTER] 3 [ENTER] 0 [ENTER] 1 [ENTER] [2nd] **[STAT PLOT]** [ENTER] [ENTER] [▼] [▶] [ENTER] [▼] [2nd] **[L1]** [ENTER] [▼] [2nd] **[L2]** [ENTER] [GRAPH] .

The vertices of a triangle with perimeter three times that of △*ABC* can be found by multiplying each coordinate of the vertices of △*ABC* by 3. Enter these vertices into **L3** and **L4**, using **L1** and **L2**.

Keystrokes: [STAT] [ENTER] [▶] [▲] 3 [2nd] **[L1]** [ENTER] [▶] [▲] 3 [2nd] **[L2]** [ENTER] .

Define **Plot2** as a connected scatter plot using **L3** and **L4**. Make sure both **Plot1** and **Plot2** are on and graph.

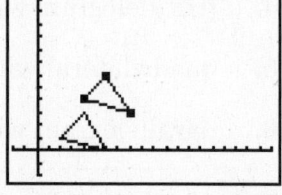

[−2, 20] scl:1 by [−2, 12] scl:1

Keystrokes: [2nd] **[STAT PLOT]** [▼] [ENTER] [ENTER] [▼] [▶] [ENTER] [▼] [2nd] **[L3]** [ENTER] [2nd] **[L4]** [ENTER] [GRAPH] .

Trace to determine the coordinates *A'*(6, 3), *B'*(12, 9), and *C'*(18, 0).

**Example 2** Translate △*ABC* 2 units right and 3 units up.

Add 2 to each coordinate in **L1** and store the result in **L3**. Then add 3 to each coordinate in **L2** and store in **L4**. Then graph the plots.
Keystrokes: [STAT] [ENTER] [▶] [▶] [▲] [2nd] **[L1]** [+] 2 [ENTER] [▶] [▲] [2nd] **[L2]** [+] 3 [ENTER] [GRAPH] .

Trace to verify the new vertices *A'*(10,6), *B'*(2,4), and *C'*(5,7).

[−2, 20] scl:1 by [−2, 12] scl:1

Lesson 10-3

### Exercises

**Find the vertices of each image for the given transformation of △*ABC* with vertices *A*(−3, 1), *B*(0, 4), and *C*(4, −2).**

**1.** dilation by a scale factor of 4

**2.** dilation by a scale factor of $\frac{1}{2}$

**3.** translation 6 units left and 2 units up

**4.** reflection over the *x*-axis

## 10-4 Lesson Reading Guide

### Quadrilaterals

### Get Ready for the Lesson

**Read the introduction to Lesson 10-4 in your textbook. Write your answers below.**

**a.** Describe the bricks used to create the smallest circles.

**b.** Describe how the shape of the bricks changes as the circles get larger.

### Read the Lesson

**Write a definition and give an example of the new vocabulary word.**

| | Vocabulary | Definition | Example |
|---|---|---|---|
| **1.** | quadrilateral | | |

**After each description, write the correct word from the list.**

trapezoid      rhombus      parallelogram      square      rectangle

**2.** a parallelogram with four right angles _____

**3.** a quadrilateral with both pairs of opposite sides parallel and congruent _____

**4.** a parallelogram with four congruent sides and four right angles _____

**5.** a quadrilateral with one pair of opposite sides parallel _____

**6.** a parallelogram with four congruent sides _____

### Remember What You Learned

**7.** The sum of the measures of the angles of a quadrilateral is 360°. Identify the quadrilaterals below and find the missing angle measure.

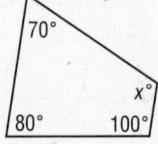
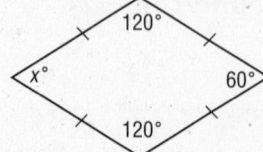
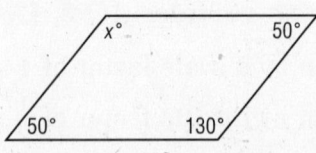

# 10-4 Study Guide and Intervention

## Quadrilaterals

A **quadrilateral** is a polygon with four sides and four vertices. The segments of a quadrilateral intersect only at their endpoints.

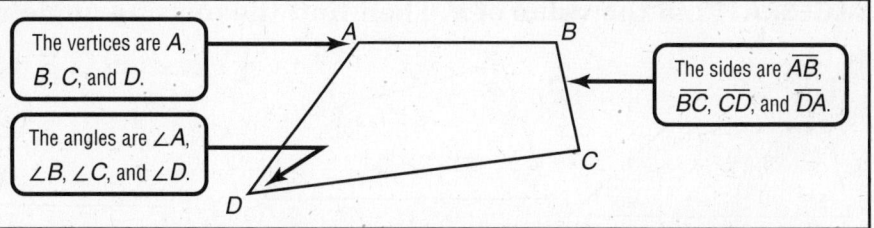

The vertices are $A$, $B$, $C$, and $D$.

The angles are $\angle A$, $\angle B$, $\angle C$, and $\angle D$.

The sides are $\overline{AB}$, $\overline{BC}$, $\overline{CD}$, and $\overline{DA}$.

A quadrilateral can be separated into two triangles. Since the sum of the measures of the angles of a triangle is 180°, the sum of the measures of the angles of a quadrilateral is 2(180°) or 360°.

### Example
**ALGEBRA  Find the value of $x$. Then find each missing angle measure.**

**Words**        The sum of the measures of the angles is 360°.

**Variable**     Let $m\angle A$, $m\angle B$, $m\angle C$, and $m\angle D$ represent the measures of the angles.

**Equation**

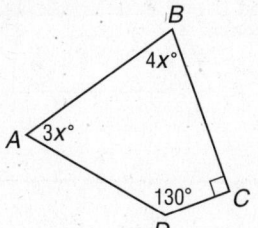

| | |
|---|---|
| $m\angle A + m\angle B + m\angle C + m\angle D = 360$ | Angles of a quadrilateral |
| $3x + 4x + 90 + 130 = 360$ | Substitution |
| $7x + 220 = 360$ | Combine like terms. |
| $7x + 220 - 220 = 360 - 220$ | Subtract 220 from each side. |
| $7x = 140$ | Simplify. |
| $x = 20$ | Divide each side by 7. |

The value of $x$ is 20. So, $m\angle A = 3(20)$ or 60° and $m\angle B = 4(20)$ or 80°.

### Exercises

**ALGEBRA  Find the value of $x$. Then find the missing angle measures.**

1.
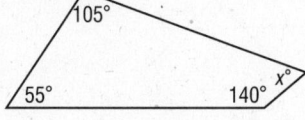

2.
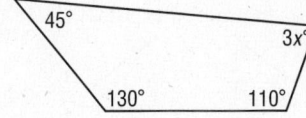

3.
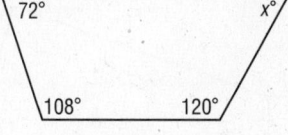

**Classify each quadrilateral using the name that *best* describes it.**

4.
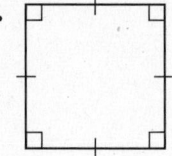

5.
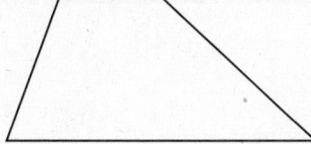

6.
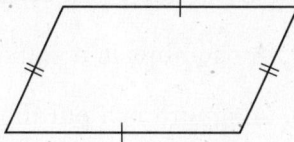

Lesson 10-4

## 10-4  Skills Practice

### *Quadrilaterals*

**ALGEBRA** Find the value of $x$. Then find the missing angle measures.

**1.**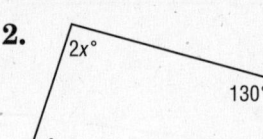

**2.**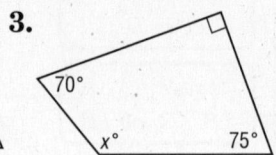

**3.**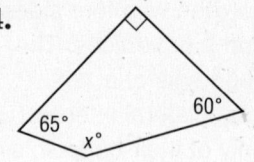

**4.**

**5.**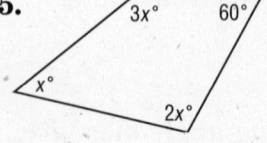

**6.**

**7.**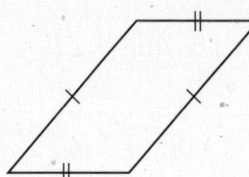

**8.**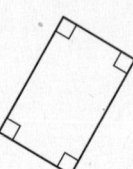

**9.**

**10.**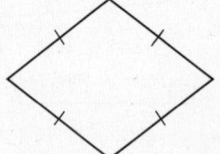

**11.**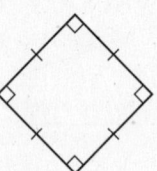

**12.**

**Classify each quadrilateral using the name that *best* describes it.**

**13.**

**14.**

**15.**

**16.**

**17.**

**18.**

**Tell whether each statement is *sometimes, always,* or *never* true.**

**19.** A rhombus is a square.

**20.** A square is a parallelogram.

**21.** A parallelogram is a square.

# 10-4 Practice

## Quadrilaterals

**ALGEBRA** Find the value of $x$. Then find the missing angle measures.

1.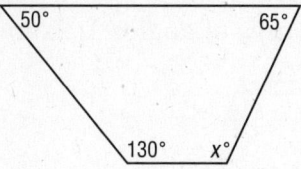

2.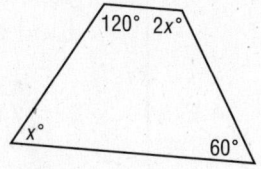

3.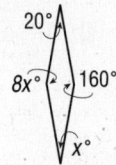

4.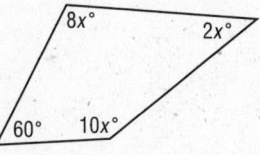

5.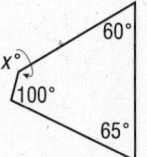

6.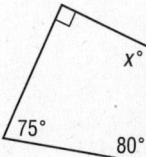

7.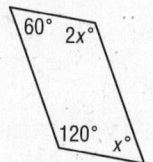

8.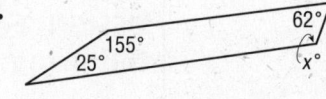

9.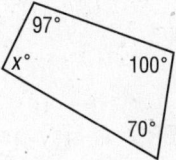

**Tell whether each statement is *sometimes*, *always*, or *never* true.**

10. A parallelogram is a trapezoid.

11. A square is a quadrilateral.

12. A rhombus is a rectangle.

13. A quadrilateral is a rectangle.

**Make a drawing of each quadrilateral. Then classify each quadrilateral using the name that *best* describes it.**

14. In quadrilateral $ACFG$, $m\angle A = 60°$, $m\angle C = 120°$, $m\angle F = 115°$, and $m\angle G = 65°$.

15. In quadrilateral $EMNP$, $m\angle E = 90°$, $m\angle M = 80°$, $m\angle N = 60°$, and $m\angle P = 130°$.

Lesson 10-4

## 10-4 Word Problem Practice

### Quadrilaterals

1. **KITES** Yashika got a new kite for her birthday. What quadrilateral best describes the shape of this kite?

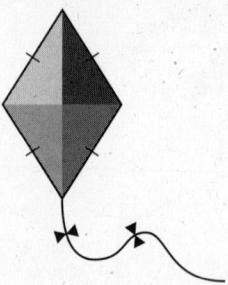

2. **PLANTERS** A city used large tree planters to line the road. Identify as many different quadrilaterals as possible in the planters.

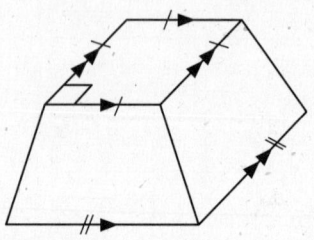

3. **PROPERTY** Mr. Orwell has some property in the middle of the wilderness. The shape of the property is a quadrilateral. Mr. Orwell knows the angles of intersections of three sides are 28°, 147°, and 72°. What is the measure of the fourth angle of the property?

4. **WINDOWS** The window above the front door in Heather's home is shown below. Find the measures of angles 1, 2, and 3.

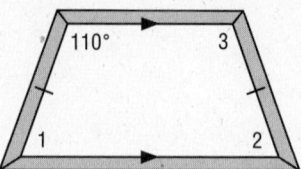

**DESIGN  For Exercises 5–7, use the following information.**

Diego is going to design a kite. Two of the opposite angles are congruent. One of the other angles is half the congruent angles, and the other is twice the congruent angles.

5. Make a sketch of the kite.

6. Write an equation to find the measures of the four angles of the kite.

7. What are the measures of the four angles?

# 10-4 Enrichment

## Using Coordinates

**For Exercises 1–4, use the coordinate grid at the right.**

1. Graph the points (1, 1), (4, 4), and (2, 4). Connect the dots. Name the figure formed.

2. Multiply each *y*-coordinate in Exercise 1 by −1. Graph the points. How is this triangle related to the one in Exercise 1?

3. Multiply each coordinate in Exercise 1 by −1. Graph the points.

4. What would you have to do to get the coordinates of a triangle in Quadrant II congruent to the ones in Excercises 1–3?

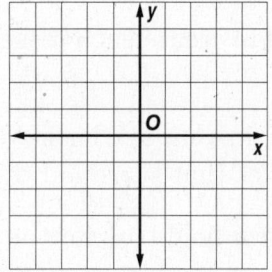

**For Exercises 5–10, use the coordinate grid at the right.**

5. Graph the points (3, 1), (2, 3), (4, 6), and (5, 4). Connect the dots. The figure formed is called a parallelogram.

6. Add 2 to both coordinates of each point and graph the new coordinates. Name the figure formed.

7. Add −4 to the *x*-coordinate of each point in Exercise 5 and graph the new coordinates. Is this figure also a parallelogram?

8. Graph the points (5, −2), (6, −3), (5, −5), and (3, −3) on the coordinate plane at the right. Name the figure formed.

9. Multiply both coordinates of each point in Exercise 8 by 2 and graph the new coordinates. This is an enlargement.

10. Multiply both coordinates of each point in Exercise 8 by $\frac{1}{2}$ and graph the new coordinates. This is a reduction.

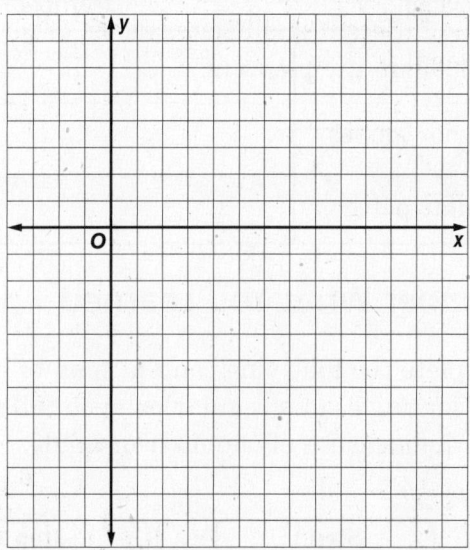

**Lesson 10-4**

## 10-5  Lesson Reading Guide

### *Polygons*

### Get Ready for the Lesson

**Read the introduction to Lesson 10-5 in your textbook. Write your answers below.**

**a.** Which figure is used to create each tessellation?


**b.** Refer to the diagram in your textbook. What is the sum of the measures of the angles that surround the vertex?

**c.** Does the sum in part **b** hold true for the square tessellation? Explain.



**d.** Make a conjecture about the sum of the measures of the angles that surround a vertex in the hexagon tessellation.

### Read the Lesson

**Write a definition and give an example of each new vocabulary word or phrase.**

| Vocabulary | Definition | Example |
|---|---|---|
| **1.** diagonal | | |
| **2.** interior angles | | |
| **3.** regular polygon | | |

### Remember What You Learned

**4.** Complete the following concept map of how to find the sum of the measures of the interior angles of a regular polygon (all sides and angles are congruent) and how to find the measure of one interior angle.

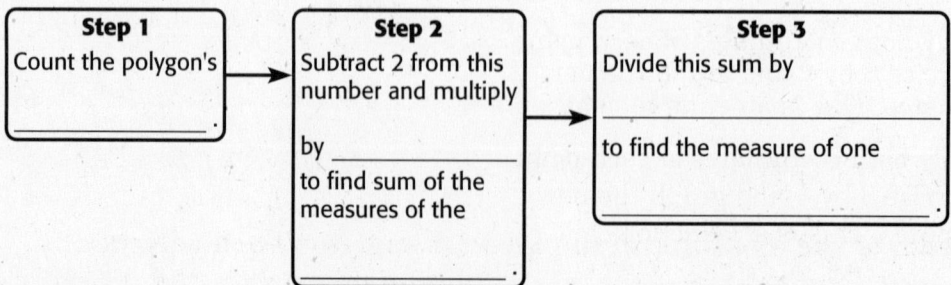

**Step 1**
Count the polygon's
_____ .

**Step 2**
Subtract 2 from this number and multiply

by _____
to find sum of the measures of the
_____

**Step 3**
Divide this sum by

_____
to find the measure of one
_____ .

# 10-5 Study Guide and Intervention

## Polygons

A **polygon** is a simple, closed figure formed by three or more coplanar line segments. The line segments, called *sides,* meet only at their endpoints. The points of intersection are called *vertices.* Polygons can be classified by the number of sides they have.

A **diagonal** is a line segment in a polygon that joins two nonconsecutive vertices, forming triangles. You can use the property of the sum of the measures of the angles of a triangle to find the sum of the measures of the interior angles of any polygon. An **interior angle** is an angle inside a polygon.

| Number of Sides | Name of Polygon |
|:---:|:---:|
| 3 | triangle |
| 4 | quadrilateral |
| 5 | pentagon |
| 6 | hexagon |
| 7 | heptagon |
| 8 | octagon |
| 9 | nonagon |
| 10 | decagon |

> If a polygon has $n$ sides, then $n - 2$ triangles are formed. The sum of the degree measures of the interior angles of the polygon is $(n - 2)180$.
>
> A regular polygon is a polygon that is *equilateral* (all sides are congruent) and *equiangular* (all angles are congruent). Since the angles of a regular polygon are congruent, their measures are equal.

**Example** **Find the measure of one interior angle of a regular 20-gon.**

**Step 1** A 20-gon has 20 sides. Therefore, $n = 20$.

$(n - 2)180 = (20 - 2)180$      Replace $n$ with 20.

$= 18(180)$ or $3240$      Simplify.

The sum of the measures of the interior angles is $3240°$.

**Step 2** Divide the sum by 20 to find the measure of one angle.

$3240 \div 20 = 162$

So, the measure of one interior angle in a regular 20-gon is $162°$.

## Exercises

**Classify each polygon. Then determine whether it appears to be *regular* or *not regular*.**

1.

2.

3.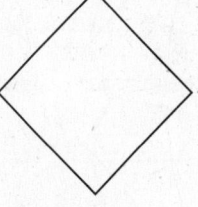

**Find the sum of the measures of the interior angles of each polygon.**

**4.** quadrilateral      **5.** nonagon      **6.** heptagon      **7.** 12-gon

Lesson 10-5

## 10-5  Skills Practice

### Polygons

Classify each polygon. Then determine whether it appears to be *regular* or *not regular*.

1.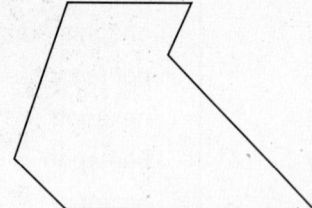

2.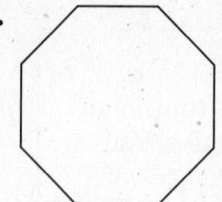

3.

4.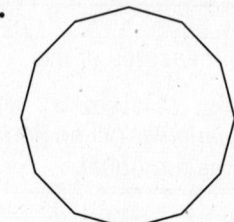

5.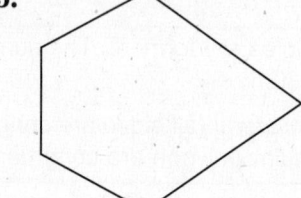

6.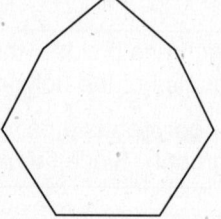

Find the sum of the measures of the interior angles of each polygon.

7. pentagon          8. 20–gon          9. nonagon          10. decagon

Find the measure of an interior angle of each polygon.

11. regular hexagon          12. regular heptagon          13. regular quadrilateral

14. regular octagon          15. regular pentagon          16. regular 100–gon

**TESSELLATIONS** For Exercises 17 and 18, identify the polygons used to create each tessellation.

17.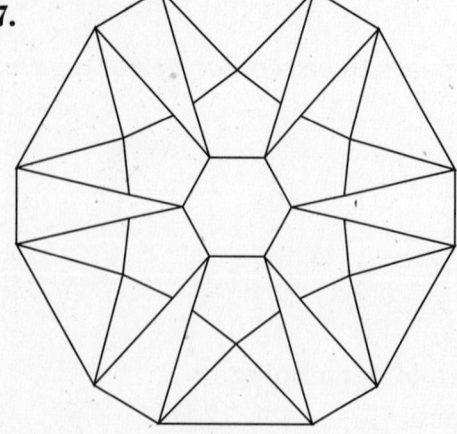

18.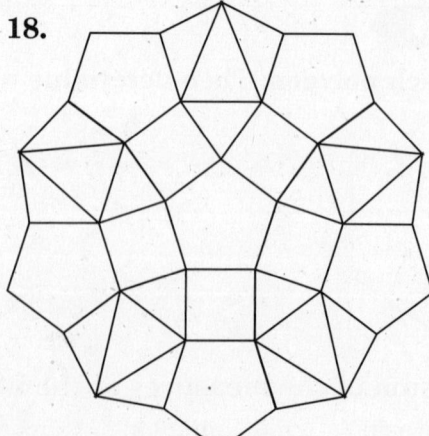

## 10-5 Practice

### Polygons

**Find the sum of the measures of the interior angles of each polygon.**

1. quadrilateral
2. decagon
3. 12-gon

4. heptagon
5. pentagon
6. hexagon

7. 25-gon
8. 100-gon

**Find the measure of an interior angle of each polygon.**

9. regular nonagon
10. regular octagon
11. regular hexagon

12. regular 12–gon
13. regular quadrilateral
14. regular decagon

**TESSELLATIONS** For Exercises 15 and 16, identify the polygons used to create each tessellation.

15.

16.

17. Which figure best represents a regular polygon?

A
B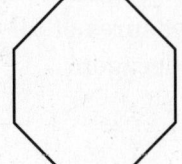
C
D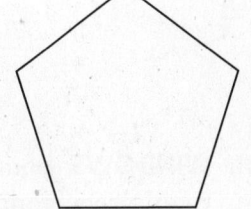

Lesson 10-5

## 10-5  Word Problem Practice

### Polygons

1. **TRAFFIC SIGNS** A familiar sight to many people is the red STOP sign found at street corners and intersections. The shape of the STOP sign is shown below. Classify the polygon and determine if it appears to be regular or not regular.

2. **NUTS AND BOLTS** The nut to a standard bolt is a regular hexagon. What is the sum of the measures of the interior angles of the nut?

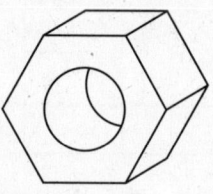

3. **WINDOWS** Some older houses have regular octagonal windows. What would be the measure of one of the interior angles in this type of window?

4. **AREA RUGS** The pattern in an area rug is shown below. Identify the three different polygons used to create the pattern.

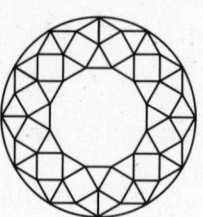

**SYMBOLS** For Exercises 5–7, use the following information.

Jenna made this shape with patterns blocks.

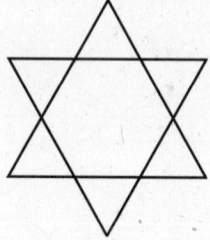

5. This design can be made up of 7 regular polygons. What are they?

6. This design is also made of one dodecagon. What is the sum of the measures of all the interior angles of the dodecagon?

7. What are the measures of the interior angles of the dodecagon?

## 10-5 Enrichment

## Polygons and Diagonals

A **diagonal** of a polygon is any segment that connects two nonconsecutive vertices of the polygon. In each of the following polygons, all possible diagonals are drawn.

**Example**

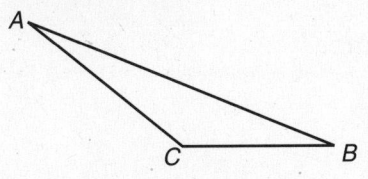

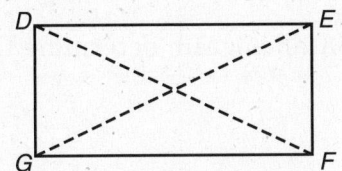

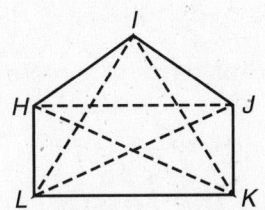

In △ABC, no diagonals can be drawn. Why?

In quadrilateral *DEFG*, 2 diagonals can be drawn.

In pentagon *HIJKL*, 5 diagonals can be drawn.

**Complete the chart below and try to find a pattern that will help you answer the questions that follow.**

| | Polygons | Number of Sides | Number of Diagonals from One Vertex | Total Number of Diagonals |
|---|---|---|---|---|
| | triangle | 3 | 0 | 0 |
| | quadrilateral | 4 | 1 | 2 |
| | pentagon | 5 | 2 | 5 |
| 1. | hexagon | 6 | | |
| 2. | heptagon | 7 | | |
| 3. | octagon | 8 | | |
| 4. | nonagon | 9 | | |
| 5. | decagon | 10 | | |

**Find the total number of diagonals that can be drawn in a polygon with the given number of sides.**

**6.** 6

**7.** 7

**8.** 8

**9.** 9

**10.** 10

**11.** 11

**12.** 12

**13.** 15

**14.** 20

**15.** 50

**16.** 75

**17.** $n$

Lesson 10–5

## 10-6  Lesson Reading Guide

### *Area: Parallelograms, Triangles, and Trapezoids*

## Get Ready for the Lesson

**Read the introduction to Lesson 10-6 in your textbook. Write your answers below.**

**a.** Compare the area of the rectangle to the area of the parallelogram.


**b.** What parts of a rectangle and parallelogram determine their area?



## Read the Lesson

**Write a definition and give an example of each new vocabulary word.**

| Vocabulary | Definition | Example |
|---|---|---|
| **1.** base | | |
| **2.** altitude | | |

## Remember What You Learned

**3.** Below are three figures and three formulas for finding area. Match the formula with the correct figure and find its area.

$A = \frac{1}{2}h(a + b)$  $\qquad\qquad$  $A = bh$  $\qquad\qquad$  $A = \frac{1}{2}bh$

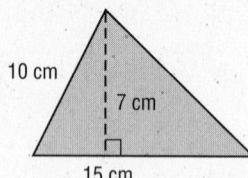

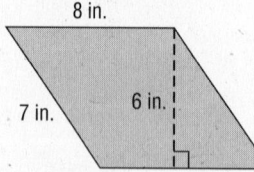

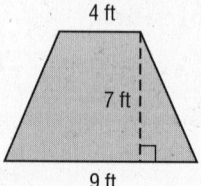

Formula: $\qquad\qquad\qquad\quad$ Formula: $\qquad\qquad\qquad\quad$ Formula:

Area: $\qquad\qquad\qquad\qquad$ Area: $\qquad\qquad\qquad\qquad\;$ Area:

# 10-6 Study Guide and Intervention

## Area: Parallelograms, Triangles, and Trapezoids

| Shape | Words | Area Formula | Model |
|---|---|---|---|
| Parallelogram | The area of a parallelogram can be found by multiplying the measures of the base and the height. | $A = bh$ | ![parallelogram with base b and height h] |
| Triangle | A diagonal of a parallelogram separates the parallelogram into two congruent triangles. The area of each triangle is one-half the area of the parallelogram. | $A = \frac{1}{2} bh$ | ![triangle with height h and base b] |
| Trapezoid | A trapezoid has two bases. The height of a trapezoid is the distance between the bases. A trapezoid can be separated into two triangles. | $A = \frac{1}{2} h(a + b)$ | ![trapezoid with top a, height h, base b] |

**Example** Find the area of the trapezoid.

$A = \frac{1}{2}h(a + b)$   Area of a trapezoid

$A = \frac{1}{2} \cdot 17(7 + 26)$   Replace $h$ with 17, $a$ with 7, and $b$ with 26.

$A = \frac{1}{2} \cdot 17 \cdot 33$   $7 + 26 = 33$

$A = \frac{561}{2}$ or $280\frac{1}{2}$

The area of the trapezoid is $280\frac{1}{2}$ mm².

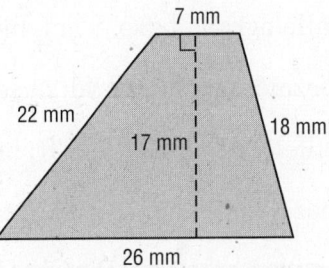

**Exercises**

Find the area of each figure.

1.
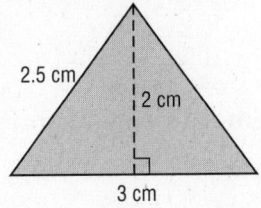

2.
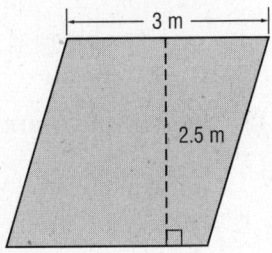

3.
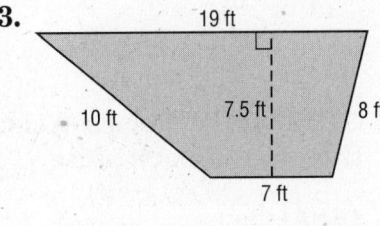

Find the area of each figure described.

4. trapezoid: height, 12 yd; bases, 6 yd, 8 yd

5. parallelogram: base, 4.5 cm; height, 8 cm

# 10-6 Skills Practice

## Area: Parallelograms, Triangles, and Trapezoids

**Find the area of each figure.**

1.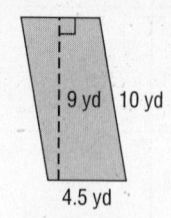
9 yd  10 yd
4.5 yd

2.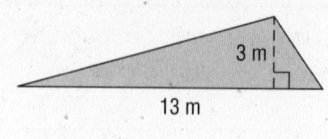
3 m
13 m

3.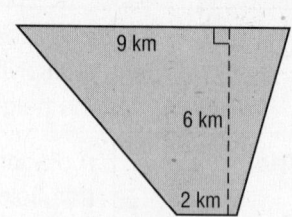
9 km
6 km
2 km

4.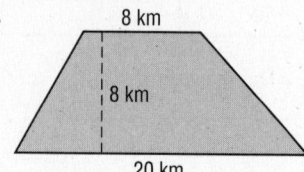
8 km
8 km
20 km

5.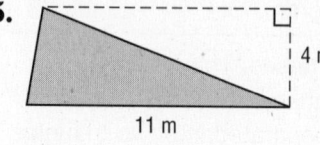
4 m
11 m

6.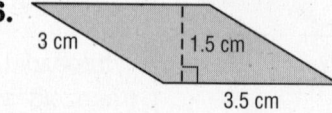
3 cm  1.5 cm
3.5 cm

**Find the area of each figure described.**

7. triangle: base, 11 m; height, 3 m

8. parallelogram: base, 8 cm; height, 9.5 cm

9. trapezoid: height, 12 yd; bases, 4 yd, 7 yd

10. parallelogram: base, 6.5 ft; height, 12 ft

11. trapezoid: height, 10 m; bases, 3 m, 6 m

12. triangle: base, 7 km; height, 5 km

**Find the area of each figure.**

13.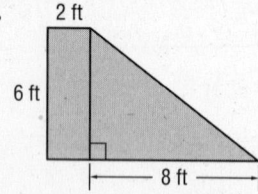
2 ft
6 ft
8 ft

14.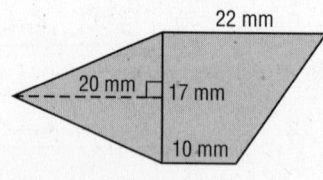
22 mm
20 mm  17 mm
10 mm

15.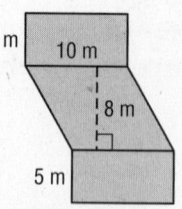
5 m  10 m
8 m
5 m

**GEOGRAPHY  For Exercises 16–18, use the approximate measurements to estimate the area of each state.**

16. Alabama
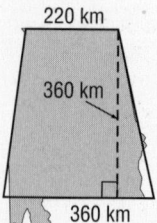
220 km
360 km
360 km

17. Florida
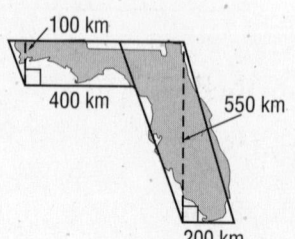
100 km
400 km  550 km
200 km

18. Nevada
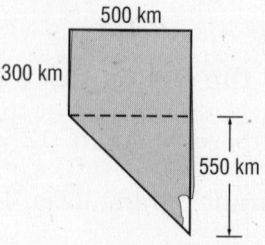
500 km
300 km
550 km

# 10-6 Practice

## Area: Parallelograms, Triangles, and Trapezoids

**Find the area of each figure described.**

1. parallelogram: base, 12 m; height, 10 m

2. trapezoid: height, 13 cm; bases, 3 cm, 7 cm

3. triangle: base, 9.4 ft; height, 5 ft

4. triangle: base, 8.5 km; height, 14 km

5. parallelogram: base, 15 yd; height, 7 yd

6. trapezoid: height, 7 m; bases, 6 m, 9 m

**Find the area of each figure.**

7.

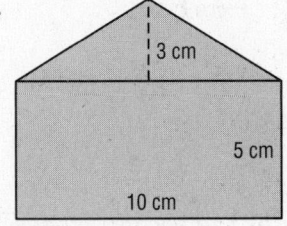

8.

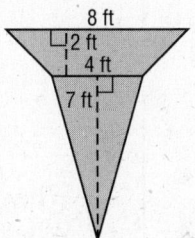

9.

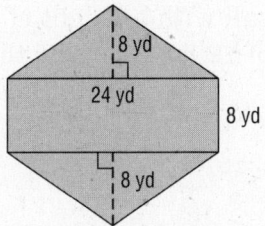

**GEOGRAPHY** For Exercises 10–12, use the approximate measurements to estimate the area of each state.

10. Maine

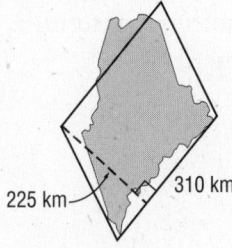

11. Idaho

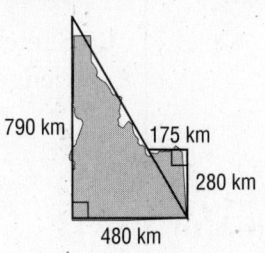

12. North Carolina

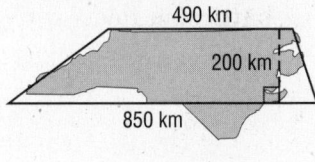

13. Suppose a triangle has an area of 220 square meters. What is the measure of the height if the base measures 20 meters?

14. A trapezoid has an area of 27.5 square centimeters. What is the measure of the height if the bases measure 7 centimeters and 4 centimeters?

15. Find the base of a parallelogram with a height of 10.5 feet and an area of 189 square feet.

# 10-6 Word Problem Practice

## Area: Parallelograms, Triangles, and Trapezoids

**1. FLOOR PLANS** Matt's bedroom is shaped like a parallelogram. His parents have decided to buy a new carpet for his room. If two opposite walls are 12 feet long and the distance between these walls is 8 feet, how many square feet of carpet will they need to buy?

**2. SAILBOATS** A sailboat has a triangular sail with a height of 18 feet and the base of 12 feet. What is the area of the sail?

**3. TILING** Mrs. Sanchez wants to tile her bathroom floor. The floor is 5 feet wide and 8 feet long. The tiles Mrs. Sanchez wants to use are 4 inch squares. How many tiles will she need to cover the bathroom floor?

**4. GLASS COSTS** Mrs. Humphrey needs to replace a broken window at her house. The window is shaped like a trapezoid with the dimensions shown below. If glass costs $4.50 per square foot, how much will the replacement window cost?

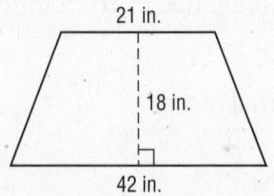

**SYMBOLS** **For Exercises 5–7, use the following information.**

Melanie wants to cut her cake into triangular wedges to serve at her party. She cannot decide what kind of triangle to cut. She tries two possible triangular wedges.

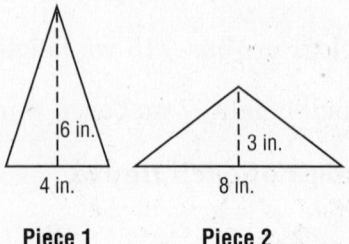

Piece 1          Piece 2

**5.** What is the area of the first wedge? What is the area of the second wedge?

**6.** Sketch and label another triangular wedge with the same area.

**7.** Melanie wants each guest to have the same amount of cake. If there are 54 guests at the party, what should the dimensions of the cake be so that everyone gets the same amount of cake?

## 10-6 Enrichment

## *Area of an Equilateral Triangle*

The area of an equilateral triangle is the product of one fourth of the square of a side times the square root of 3 (which is approximately 1.732).

$$A = \frac{1}{4} s^2 (\sqrt{3})$$

or $A \approx \frac{s^2}{4} (1.732)$

**Example**

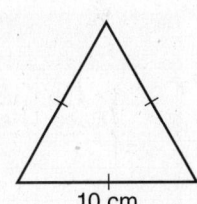

$A \approx \frac{10^2}{4} (1.732)$

$\approx \frac{100}{4} (1.732)$

$\approx 43.3$

The area of the triangle is approximately 43.3 cm².

**Find the area of each equilateral triangle. Round each answer to the nearest tenth.**

1.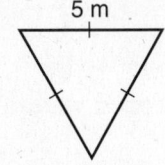
5 m

2.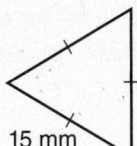
15 mm

3.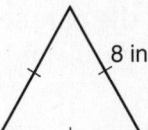
8 in.

4.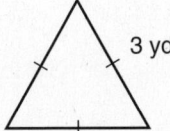
3 yd

5.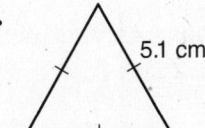
5.1 cm

6.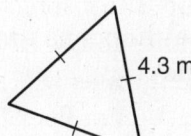
4.3 m

7.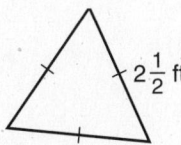
$2\frac{1}{2}$ ft

8.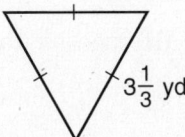
$3\frac{1}{3}$ yd

9.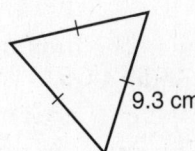
9.3 cm

10.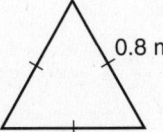
0.8 m

11.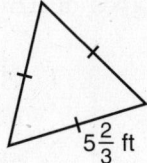
$5\frac{2}{3}$ ft

12.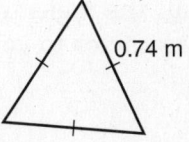
0.74 m

# 10-6  Spreadsheet Activity

## Maximum Area of a Parallelogram

You can use cardboard strips, paper fasteners, and a spreadsheet to investigate how changing the height of a parallelogram with a fixed perimeter changes the area of the parallelogram.

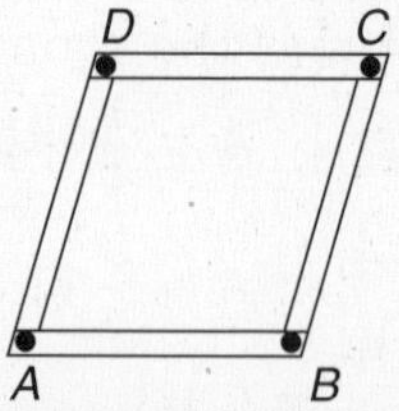

**Step 1**  Cut two pairs of cardboard strips. Construct a parallelogram by fastening the strips together at the corners as shown at the right. Label the vertices *A*, *B*, *C*, and *D*.

**Step 2**  Move the sides of the parallelogram so that the measure of angle *A* is small. Use a centimeter ruler to measure the base and the height of the parallelogram. Enter the data in Columns A and B of the spreadsheet. Use Column C for the formula for the area of the parallelogram.

| ◇ | A | B | C | |
|---|------|--------|--------|---|
| 1 | Base | Height | Area | |
| 2 | | | =A2*B2 | |
| 3 | | | =A3*B3 | |
| 4 | | | =A4*B4 | |

Sheet 1 / Sheet 2

**Step 3**  Move the sides of the parallelogram to increase the measure of angle *A* and measure the base and the height again. Record the data. Continue changing the parallelogram, measuring and recording data until you have at least 6 different pairs of measures.

## Exercises

**Refer to the spreadsheet.**

1. What happens to the measure of the base as you increase the measure of angle *A*?

2. What happens to the measure of the height as you increase the measure of angle *A*?

3. How is the area of the parallelogram affected as you increase the measure of angle *A*?

4. Notice that since the sides of parallelogram *ABCD* are fixed, the perimeter is unchanged as the measure of angle *A* is changed. Make a conjecture about the measure of angle *A* when the area of *ABCD* is the greatest. Use a protractor to verify your conjecture.

# 10-7 Lesson Reading Guide

## Circles: Circumference and Area

### Get Ready for the Lesson

**Read the introduction to Lesson 10-7 in your textbook. Write your answers below.**

**a.** Collect three different-sized circular objects. Then copy the table shown.

**b.** Using a tape measure, measure each distance below to the nearest millimeter. Record your results.

  • the distance across the circular object through its center ($d$)

  • the distance around each circular object ($C$)

**c.** For each object, find the ratio $\dfrac{C}{d}$. Record the results in the table.

**d.** Write an equation that relates circumference $C$ of a circle to its diameter $d$.

### Read the Lesson

**Write a definition and give an example of each new vocabulary word.**

| Vocabulary | Definition | Example |
|---|---|---|
| **1.** circle | | |
| **2.** diameter | | |
| **3.** center | | |
| **4.** circumference | | |
| **5.** radius | | |
| **6.** $\pi$ (pi) | | |

### Remember What You Learned

**7.** Study the circle at the right, label each part, then find the circle's circumference and area (round to the nearest tenth).

formula for circumference:

formula for area:

circumference:

area:

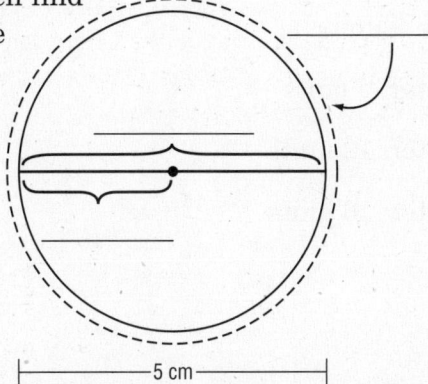

5 cm

Lesson 10–7

# 10-7 Study Guide and Intervention

## Circles: Circumference and Area

| Circles | The **circumference** of a circle is equal to its diameter times $\pi$, or 2 times its radius times $\pi$. | $C = \pi d$ or $C = 2\pi r$ |
| --- | --- | --- |
| A **circle** is the set of all points in a plane that are the same distance from a given point. | The area of a circle is equal to $\pi$ times the square or its radius. | $A = \pi r^2$ |

### Example 1

Find the circumference of the circle to the nearest tenth.

a.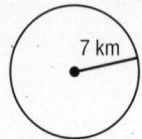

$C = 2\pi r$     Circumference of a circle

$C = 2 \cdot \pi \cdot 7$     Replace $r$ with 7.

$C \approx 44.0$     Simplify. Use a calculator.

The circumference is about 44.0 kilometers.

### Example 2

Find the area of the circle. Round to the nearest tenth.

b.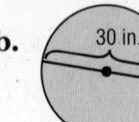

$A = \pi r^2$     Area of a circle

$A = \pi \cdot (15)^2$     Replace $r$ with 15.

$A = \pi \cdot 225$     Evaluate $(15)^2$.

$A \approx 706.9$     Use a calculator.

The area is about 706.9 square inches.

### Exercises

Find the circumference and area of each circle. Round to the nearest tenth.

1.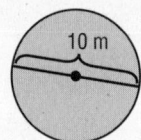
2.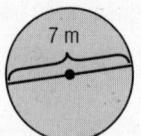
3.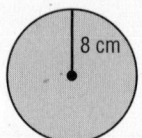
4.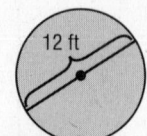

Match each circle described in the column on the left with its corresponding measurement in the column on the right.

5. radius: 5 units

6. diameter: 9 units

7. diameter: 12 units

8. diameter: 16 units

a. area: 63.6 units$^2$

b. circumference: 50.3 units

c. circumference: 31.4 units

d. area: 113.1 units$^2$

# 10-7 Skills Practice

## Circles: Circumference and Area

**Find the circumference and area of each circle. Round to the nearest tenth.**

1. 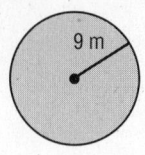 9 m

2. 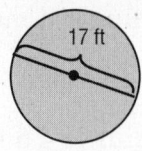 17 ft

3. 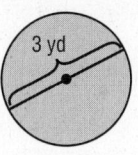 3 yd

4. 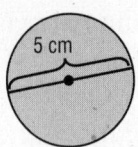 5 cm

5. The radius is 7 kilometers.

6. The diameter is 20 centimeters.

7. The diameter is 8.5 meters.

8. The radius is 11 yards.

9. The diameter is $6\frac{2}{5}$ feet.

10. The radius is 25 inches.

**Match each circle described in the column on the left with its corresponding measurement in the column on the right.**

11. diameter: 6 units

   a. area: 19.6 units$^2$

12. radius: 9 units

   b. circumference: 40.8 units

13. diameter: 13 units

   c. area: 28.3 units$^2$

14. radius: 2.5 units

   d. circumference: 56.5 units

15. **SPORTS** A basketball goal is 18 inches in diameter. A basketball has a diameter of about 9.6 inches. What is the difference in area between the goal and the center cross-section of a basketball?

16. **CULTURE** The Navajo and Pueblo Indians create large, circular sand paintings as part of traditional healing ceremonies. How much more area does a sand painting with a 20-foot diameter have compared with one with a 5-foot diameter?

17. **SPORT** In bowling, the distance from the foul line to the headpin is 60 feet. A bowling ball has a radius of about 4.3 inches. How many times must the ball rotate in order to strike the headpin?

**Find the area of each figure. Round to the nearest tenth.**

18.

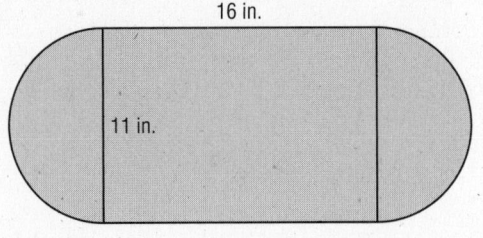

16 in.

11 in.

19.

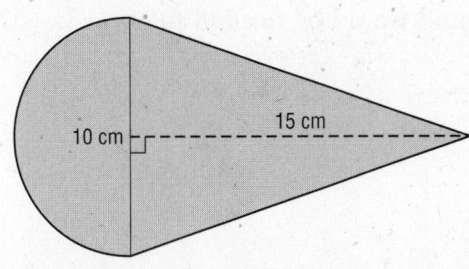

10 cm    15 cm

Lesson 10-7

# 10-7 Practice

## Circles: Circumference and Area

**Find the circumference and area of each circle. Round to the nearest tenth.**

1. The diameter is 18 yards.

2. The radius is 4 meters.

3. The diameter is 4.2 meters.

4. The radius is 4.5 feet.

5. The radius is $9\frac{3}{4}$ miles.

6. The diameter is 6 kilometers.

**Match each circle described in the column on the left with its corresponding measurement in the column on the right.**

7. radius: 8.5 units

    **a.** circumference: 53.4 units

8. diameter: 9 units

    **b.** area: 33.2 units$^2$

9. diameter: 6.5 units

    **c.** area: 63.6 units$^2$

10. radius: 12 units

    **d.** circumference: 75.4 units

11. **SPORTS** A baseball has a radius of about 1.5 inches. Home plate is 16 inches wide. If a baseball were rolled across home plate, how many complete rotations would it take to cover the distance?

12. **SPORTS** A soccer ball has a circumference of about 28 inches, while the goal is 24 feet wide. How many soccer balls would be needed to cover the distance between the goalposts?

13. **HISTORY** Chariot races reached their peak in popularity in ancient Rome around the 1st and 2nd centuries A.D. A chariot wheel had a radius of about one foot. One lap around the track in the Circus Maximus was approximately 2,300 feet. How many chariot-wheel revolutions did it take to complete one lap?

14. **CULTURE** One of the artistic traditions of Tantric Buddhism is *dul–tson–kyil–khor*, which is the creation of intricately designed prayer circles (called mandalas) using colored sand. The sand is funneled through a hollow metal tube about 0.5 centimeter in diameter. If the prayer circle were a meter across, approximately how many funnel-tips of sand would be needed to cover its surface?

# 10-7 Word Problem Practice

## Circles: Circumference and Area

1. **TREES** A tree on Joanne's property has a circumference of 6.8 feet. What is the diameter of the tree?

2. **DOGS** Carl's dog, Buddy, is on an 8-foot leash that is attached to the center of a 20-foot fence. How much space does Buddy have to roam around?

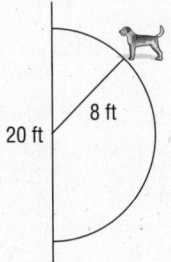

3. **KITCHEN FURNITURE** Mr. Margulies bought four new stools for his kitchen. Each stool top has a diameter of 14 inches. Mr. Margulies wants to make pads for each stool. The padding is three cents per square inch. How much will Mr. Margulies spend in padding for the four stools?

4. **TOYS** Josh has a large plastic disc that he uses to play catch with his dog. The disc has a radius of 6 inches. What is the area of the disc?

**PIZZA For Exercises 5–7, use the following information.**

At Paco's Pizza Shop, a large pizza has a diameter of 16 inches. A small pizza has a diameter of 12 inches.

5. What is the area of the small pizza? What is the area of the large pizza?

6. A large pizza costs $9.95 and a small pizza costs $5.95. Which pizza is a better deal? Explain.

7. On Tuesday's, Paco's Pizza has a special, two small pizzas for $11.25. Is this truly a special price? Explain your reasoning.

## 10-7 Enrichment

## Sector of a Circle

The sector of a circle is the region bounded by two radii and the arc of the circle. The area of a sector is a fractional part of the area of the circle.

$A = \frac{n}{360} \times \pi \times r^2$ where $n$ is the degree measure of the central angle.

**Example**

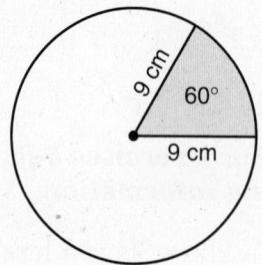

Area of a sector $\approx \frac{60}{360} \times 3.14 \times 81$

$\approx 42.39$ cm$^2$

**Find the area of each sector. Use 3.14 for $\pi$.**

1.

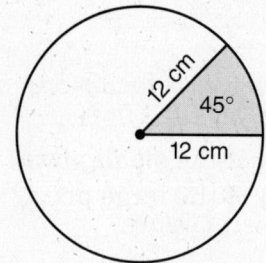

2.

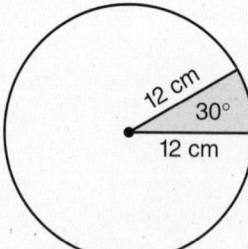

3.

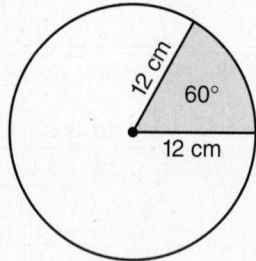

4.

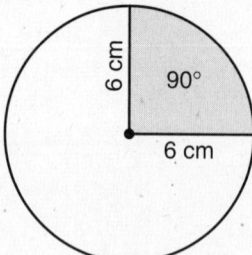

5.

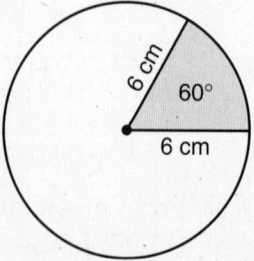

6.

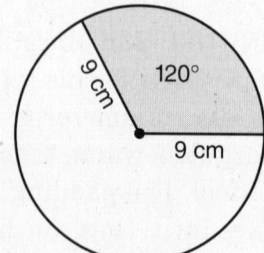

# 10-8  Lesson Reading Guide

## Area: Composite Figures

### Get Ready for the Lesson

**Read the introduction to Lesson 10-8 in your textbook. Write your answers below.**

In the diagram, the area of California is separated into polygons.

**a.** Identify the polygons.

**b.** Explain how polygons can be used to estimate the total land area.

**c.** What is the area of each region?

**d.** What is the total area?

### Read the Lesson

**Complete the following statements by filling in the blanks with the following words or symbols.**

| | | | | |
|---|---|---|---|---|
| triangle | $A = \frac{1}{2}h(a + b)$ | separating | formula | $A = bh$ |
| trapezoid | $A = \pi r^2$ | area | composite figure | |

1. The area of a(n) _____ can be determined by _____ the figure into simple polygons.

2. Each separate polygon has a specific _____ to determine its area. For a circle, it's _____ , while $A = \frac{1}{2}bh$ works for a _____ .

3. To find the area of a parallelogram, the formula _____ should be applied.

4. A(n) _____ , on the other hand, requires the formula _____ .

5. To find the _____ of the whole figure, the areas of the polygons are added together.

### Remember What You Learned

6. Study the figure below, identify the separate polygons, find the area of each polygon, and find the area of the entire figure. Round to the nearest tenth.

area of polygon 1: _____

area of polygon 2: _____

area of polygon 3: _____

total area of figure: _____

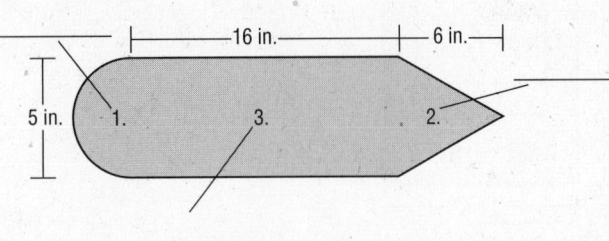

Lesson 10-8

## 10-8  Study Guide and Intervention

### Area: Composite Figures

To find the area of a composite figure, separate the composite figure into figures whose area you know how to find. Use the area formulas you have learned in this chapter.

| Triangle | Trapezoid | Parallelogram | Circle |
|---|---|---|---|
| $A = \frac{1}{2}bh$ | $A = \frac{1}{2}h(a + b)$ | $A = bh$ | $A = \pi r^2$ |

**Example**  Find the area of each figure. Round to the nearest tenth, if necessary.

a.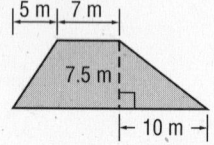

b.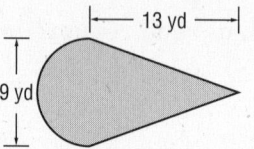

| Area of Parallelogram | Area of Triangle | Area of Semicircle | Area of Triangle |
|---|---|---|---|
| $A = bh$ | $A = \frac{1}{2}bh$ | $A = \frac{1}{2}\pi r^2$ | $A = \frac{1}{2}bh$ |
| $A = 7(7.5)$ or $52.5$ | $A = \frac{1}{2}(15 \cdot 7.5)$ | $A = \frac{1}{2}\pi(4.5)^2$ | $A = \frac{1}{2}(9 \cdot 13)$ |
| | $A = 56.25$ | $A = 31.8$ | $A = 58.5$ |

The area of the figure is $52.5 + 56.25$ or about $108.8$ m$^2$.

The area of the figure is $31.8 + 58.5$ or about $90.3$ yd$^2$.

**Exercises**

**Find the area of each figure. Round to the nearest tenth, if necessary.**

1. What is the area of a figure formed using a rectangle with a base of 10 yards and a height of 4 yards and two semicircles, one with a radius of 5 yards and the other a radius of 2 yards?

2. Find the area of a figure formed using a square and three triangles all with sides of 9 centimeters. Each triangle has a height of 6 centimeters.

**Find the area of each shaded region. Round to the nearest tenth. (*Hint:* Find the total area and subtract the non-shaded area.)**

3.

4.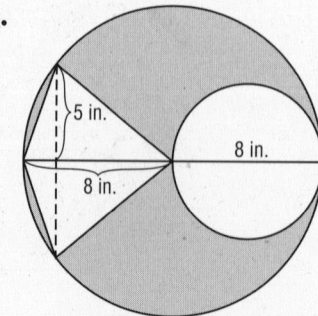

5.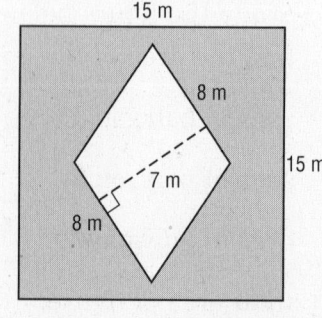

# 10-8 Skills Practice

## Area: Composite Figures

**Find the area of each figure. Round to the nearest tenth.**

**1.**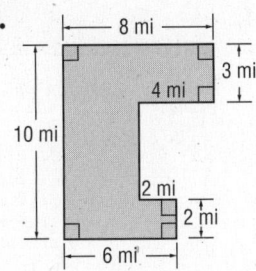

**2.**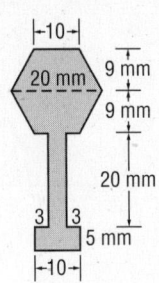

**3.**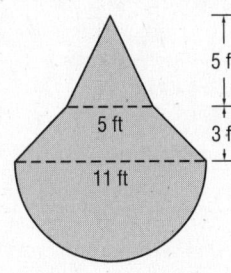

**4.**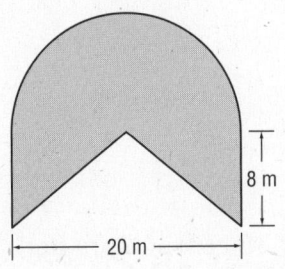

**5.**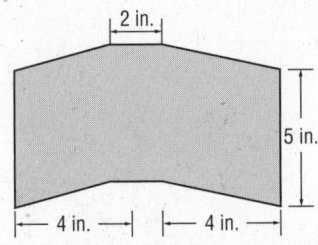

**6.**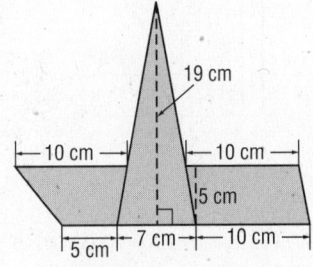

**7.**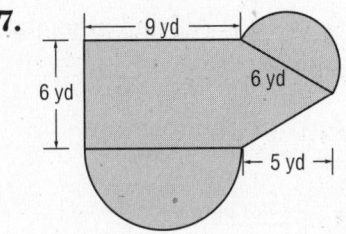

**8.**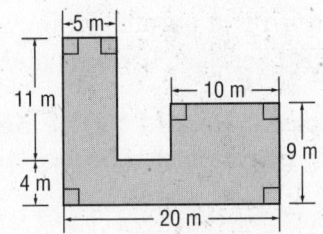

**9.**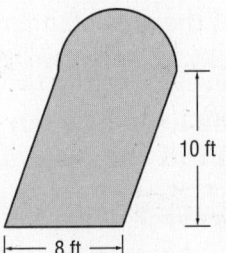

**10.** What is the area of a figure formed using a square with sides of 12 kilometers and three circles with diameters of 12 kilometers each?

**Find the area of each shaded area. Round to the nearest tenth, if necessary. (*Hint:* Find the total area and subtract the non-shaded area.)**

**11.**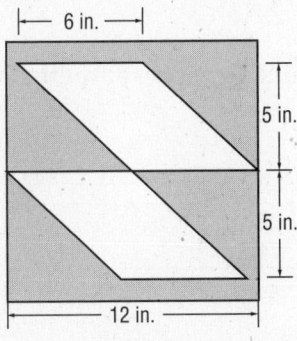

**12.**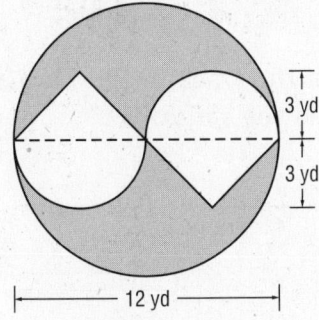

**13.**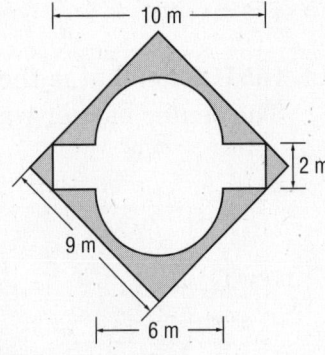

Lesson 10-8

**10-8 Practice**

### Area: Composite Figures

Find the area of each figure to the nearest tenth, if necessary.

1. 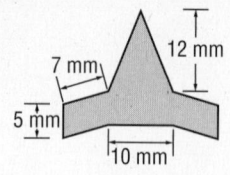  2. 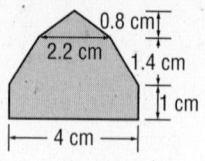  3. 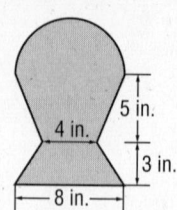  4.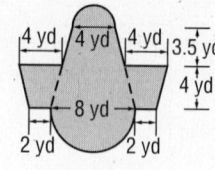

5. 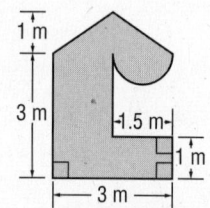  6. 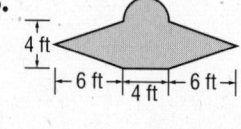  7. 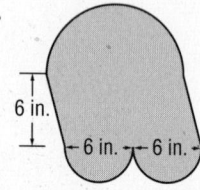  8.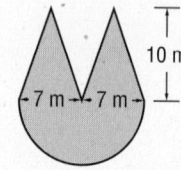

9. What is the area of a figure formed using a square with sides of 15 centimeters and four attached semicircles?

10. Find the area of a figure formed using a parallelogram with a base of 10 yards and a height of 12 yards and two triangles with bases of 10 yards and heights of 5 yards.

Find the area of each shaded area. Round to the nearest tenth, if necessary. (*Hint:* Find the total area and subtract the non-shaded area.)

11. 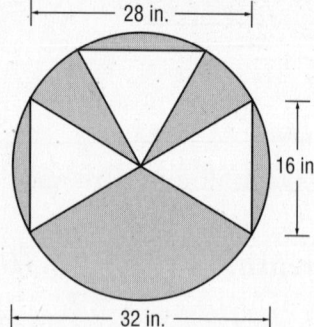  12. 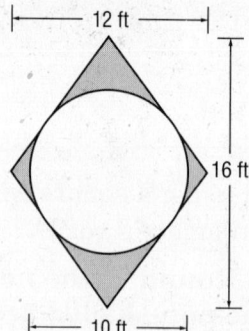  13.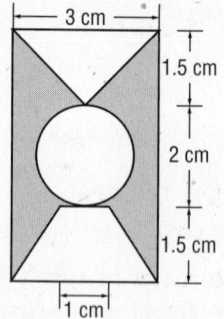

14. **HISTORY** What is the area of the track in the Circus Maximus as represented below? The center barrier was named the *spina*.

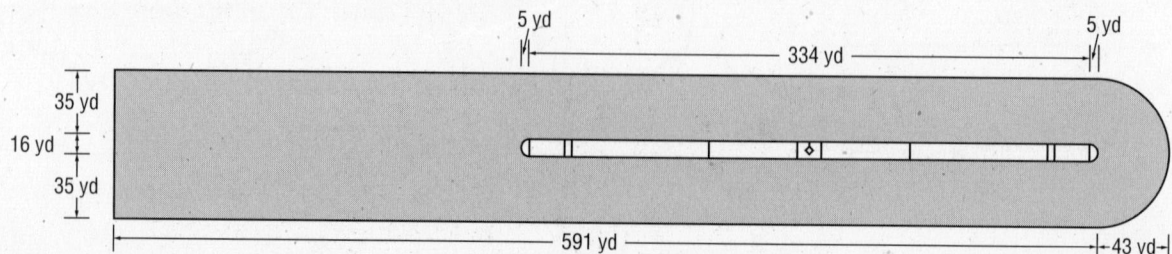

## 10-8 Word Problem Practice

### Area: Composite Figures

**1. SHELVING** The back of a shelving unit is shown below. How much plywood is needed to construct this piece of the unit? Round to the nearest whole number.

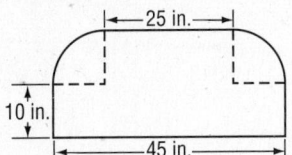

**2. LANDSCAPING** Peter's backyard is rectangular in shape, with dimensions 60 feet by 50 feet. He plans to install a circular above ground pool that has a diameter of 20 feet. What will be the area of his backyard that is left after installing the pool? Round to the nearest whole number.

**3. DOG HOUSES** Barbara is going to paint the front of her dog's house green. If one quart of paint covers 8 square feet, will she need more than one quart?

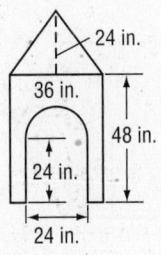

**4. LOGOS** The logo for Super Soda Company is shown below. What is the area of the shaded region?

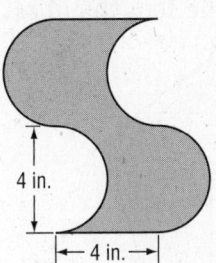

**BOATS For Exercises 5 and 6, use the following information.**

Frank is using a template to make a boat cover out of canvas for his boat. The template is shown below.

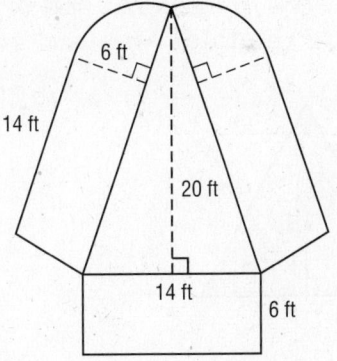

**5.** How many square feet of canvas will he need to make the template?

**6.** If canvas costs $8.00 a square yard, how much will the canvas cost?

**53**

Lesson 10-8

# 10-8 Enrichment

## Area of a Regular Polygon

The area of a regular polygon is equal to one-half the product of the **apothem** and the **perimeter**. The apothem is the distance from the center of the polygon to a side. The perimeter is the sum of the lengths of all of the sides.

**Example**

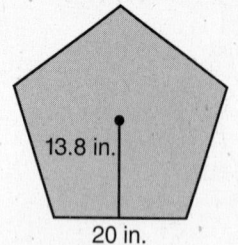

$A = \frac{1}{2} ap$  $a = 13.8, p = 100$

$= \frac{1}{2}(13.8) \cdot (100)$

$= 690 \text{ in}^2$

**Find the area of each regular polygon.**

1.
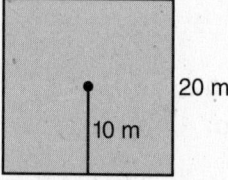
20 m
10 m

2.
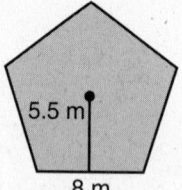
5.5 m
8 m

3.
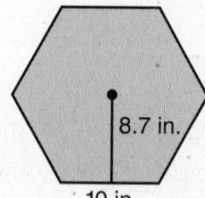
8.7 in.
10 in.

4.
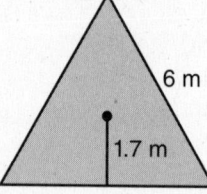
6 m
1.7 m

5.
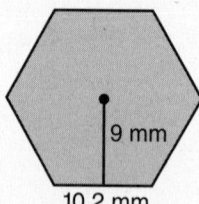
9 mm
10.2 mm

6.
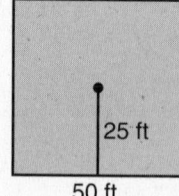
25 ft
50 ft

7.
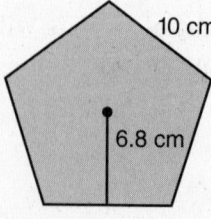
10 cm
6.8 cm

8.
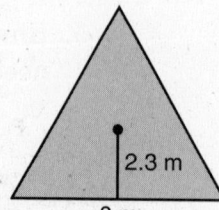
2.3 m
8 m

9.
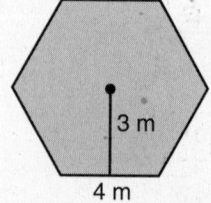
3 m
4 m

# 10 Student Recording Sheet

*Use this recording sheet with pages 570–571 of the Student Edition.*

**Read each question. Then fill in the correct answer.**

1. Ⓐ Ⓑ Ⓒ Ⓓ

2. Ⓕ Ⓖ Ⓗ Ⓙ

3. Record your answer and fill in the bubbles in the grid below. Be sure to use the correct place value.

6. Record your answer and fill in the bubbles in the grid below. Be sure to use the correct place value.

7. Ⓐ Ⓑ Ⓒ Ⓓ

8. Ⓕ Ⓖ Ⓗ Ⓙ

9. Ⓐ Ⓑ Ⓒ Ⓓ

4. Ⓐ Ⓑ Ⓒ Ⓓ

10. Ⓕ Ⓖ Ⓗ Ⓙ

11. Ⓐ Ⓑ Ⓒ Ⓓ

5. Ⓕ Ⓖ Ⓗ Ⓙ

**Pre-AP**

**Record your answers for Question 12 on the back of this paper.**

Assessment

# 10 Rubric for Scoring Pre-AP

*(Use to score the Pre-AP question on page 571 of the Student Edition.)*

## General Scoring Guidelines

- If a student gives only a correct numerical answer to a problem but does not show how he or she arrived at the answer, the student will be awarded only 1 credit. All extended response questions require the student to show work.

- A fully correct answer for a multiple-part question requires correct responses for all parts of the question. For example, if a question has three parts, the correct response to one or two parts of the question that required work to be shown is *not* considered a fully correct response.

- Students who use trial and error to solve a problem must show their method. Merely showing that the answer checks or is correct is not considered a complete response for full credit.

## Exercise 12 Rubric

| Score | Specific Criteria |
|---|---|
| 4 | A correct solution that is supported by well-developed, accurate explanations. All three translations and reflections are graphed and correctly identified with labels. The coordinates $\triangle JKM$ after a translation 2 units left and 3 units down are the vertices of $\triangle J'K'M'$ $(-5, 1)$, $(-4, -2)$, and $(-3, -1)$. The coordinates of $\triangle J'K'M'$ after a translation over the $y$-axis are the vertices of $\triangle J''K''M''$ $(5, 1)$, $(4, -2)$, and $(3, -1)$. On a separate sheet of grid paper should be the coordinates of the vertices of $\triangle JKM$ after a reflection over the $y$-axis are the vertices of $\triangle J'K'M'$ $(3, 4)$, $(2, 1)$, and $(1, 2)$. |
| 3 | A generally correct solution, but may contain minor flaws in reasoning or computation. |
| 2 | A partially correct interpretation and/or solution to the problem. |
| 1 | A correct solution with no supporting evidence or explanation. |
| 0 | An incorrect solution indicating no mathematical understanding of the concept or task, or no solution is given. |

# 10 Chapter 10 Quiz 1

*(Lessons 10-1 and 10-2)*

**In the figure at the right, $\ell \parallel m$ and $p$ is a transversal. If $m\angle 2 = 85°$, find the measure of each angle.**

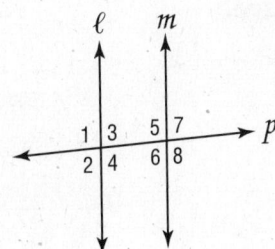

1. $\angle 3$

2. $\angle 5$

3. $\angle 8$

4. **Standardized Test Practice**
   If $m\angle A = 73°$ and $\angle A$ and $\angle B$ are supplementary, what is $m\angle B$?

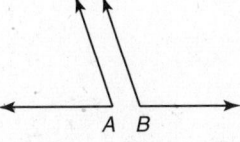

   **A.** $17°$     **C.** $73°$
   **B.** $107°$    **D.** $180°$

5. If $\triangle LMN \cong \triangle WXZ$, which segment is congruent to $\overline{NL}$?

1. _____

2. _____

3. _____

4. _____

5. _____

---

# 10 Chapter 10 Quiz 2

*(Lessons 10-3 and 10-4)*

1. Suppose the figure graphed is reflected over the *x*-axis. Find the coordinates of the vertices after the reflection.

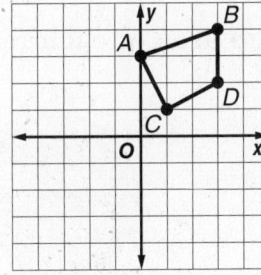

1. _____

2. Tell whether the transformation at the right is a translation, a rotation, or a reflection.

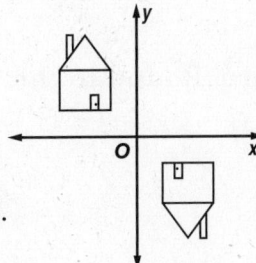

2. _____

3. In quadrilateral $ABCD$, $m\angle A = 100°$, $m\angle B = 80°$, and $m\angle C = 60°$. Find $m\angle D$.

3. _____

4. Which type of quadrilateral has exactly one pair of parallel sides?

4. _____

5. Name a sport that is played on a court that is shaped like a rectangle. Explain why the court is called a rectangle.

5. _____

Assessment

**10** **Chapter 10 Quiz 3**

SCORE _____

*(Lessons 10-5 and 10-6)*

**Find the area of each figure.**

1.

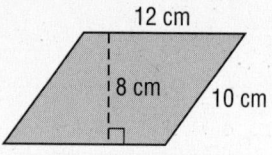

12 cm
8 cm
10 cm

2.

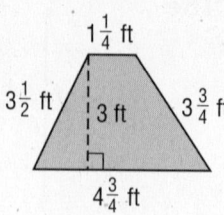

$1\frac{1}{4}$ ft
$3\frac{1}{2}$ ft   3 ft   $3\frac{3}{4}$ ft
$4\frac{3}{4}$ ft

1. _____

2. _____

3.

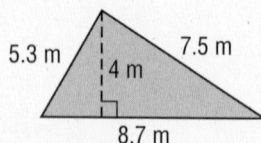

5.3 m   7.5 m
4 m
8.7 m

3. _____

4. Juan paints a coat of arms shaped like a regular hexagon.
How many sides does the painting have?

4. _____

5. Find the measure of an interior angle in a regular pentagon.

5. _____

---

**10** **Chapter 10 Quiz 4**

SCORE _____

*(Lessons 10-7 and 10-8)*

**Find the circumference and area of each figure. Round to the nearest tenth.**

1.

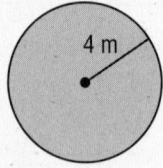

4 m

2.

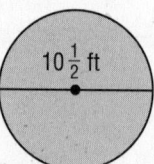

$10\frac{1}{2}$ ft

1. _____

2. _____

3. The radius is 0.7 feet.

3. _____

**Find the area of each figure. Round to the nearest tenth, if necessary.**

4.

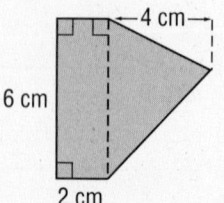

←4 cm→
6 cm
2 cm

4. _____

5. A figure that is formed using a square with sides
9 meters and a half-circle with a radius of 3.6 meters.

5. _____

# 10 Chapter 10 Mid-Chapter Test

SCORE _____

*(Lessons 10-1 through 10-4)*

**Part I** *Write the letter for the correct answer in the blank at the right of each question.*

In the figure at the right, $\ell \parallel m$ and $c$ is a transversal. Use the figure for Questions 1 and 2.

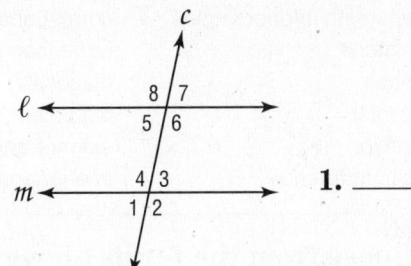

1. If $m\angle 5 = 78°$, find $m\angle 3$.
   - **A.** 102°
   - **C.** 78°
   - **B.** 12°
   - **D.** cannot be determined

   1. _____

2. If $m\angle 5 = 78°$, find $m\angle 2$.
   - **F.** 102°
   - **H.** 78°
   - **G.** 12°
   - **J.** cannot be determined

   2. _____

3. If $\triangle ABC \cong \triangle TSR$, which line segment is congruent to $\overline{BC}$?
   - **A.** $\overline{SR}$
   - **B.** $\overline{TR}$
   - **C.** $\overline{TS}$
   - **D.** $\overline{AB}$

   3. _____

4. If $\triangle MNP \cong \triangle BCD$, which angle is congruent to $\angle D$?
   - **F.** $\angle M$
   - **G.** $\angle P$
   - **H.** $\angle N$
   - **J.** $\angle B$

   4. _____

5. Angles $K$ and $S$ are complementary. Find $m\angle S$ if $m\angle K = 28°$.
   - **A.** 28°
   - **B.** 118°
   - **C.** 72°
   - **D.** 62°

   5. _____

**Part II**

6. Angles $G$ and $H$ are supplementary. Find $m\angle H$ if $m\angle G = 45°$. 6. _____

7. Triangle $TUZ$ has vertices $T(-2, 0)$, $U(1, -2)$, and $Z(2, 1)$. Graph the image of $TUZ$ after a translation 3 units right and 2 units up.

7.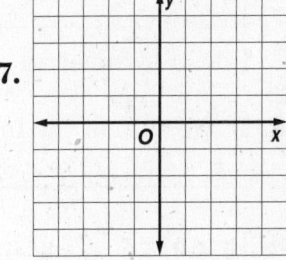

Use the figure at the right for Questions 8–10.

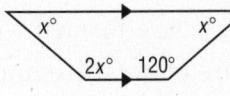

8. Classify the quadrilateral using the name that *best* describes it.

8. _____

9. Find the value of $x$.

9. _____

10. Find the missing angle measures.

10. _____

Assessment

# 10 Chapter 10 Vocabulary Test

| | | | |
|---|---|---|---|
| adjacent angles | complementary angles | line of symmetry | regular polygon |
| alternate exterior angle | congruent | parallel lines | rotation |
| alternate interior angles | corresponding angles | perpendicular lines | supplementary angles |
| altitude | corresponding parts | π (pi) | transformation |
| base | diagonal | polygon | translation |
| center | diameter | quadrilateral | transversal |
| circle | exterior angles | radius | vertical angles |
| circumference | interior angles | reflection | |

**Choose from the terms above to complete each sentence.**

1. The distance around a circle is called the

   _____.                                  1. _____

2. Figures are _____ when they have the
   same size and shape.                                        2. _____

3. The _____ is the distance across a
   circle through its center.                                  3. _____

4. Lines that intersect to form a right angle are called

   _____.                                  4. _____

5. A(n) _____ is a simple, closed figure
   formed by three or more line segments.                      5. _____

6. A closed figure with four sides and four vertices is a(n)

   _____.                                  6. _____

7. In a(n) _____, you flip a figure over a
   line of symmetry.                                           7. _____

8. If the sum of the measures of two angles is 180°, the angles are

   _____.                                  8. _____

9. In a(n) _____, you slide a figure from
   one position to another without turning it.                 9. _____

10. _____ are formed when two lines
    intersect, forming two pairs of opposite angles.          10. _____

**Define each term in your own words.**

11. transversal

12. π (pi)

**10**   **Chapter 10 Test, Form 1**

*Write the letter for the correct answer in the blank at the right of each question.*

In the figure at the right, $\ell \parallel m$ and $t$ is a transversal. Use the figure for Questions 1 and 2.

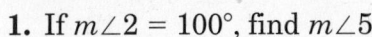

1. If $m\angle 2 = 100°$, find $m\angle 5$.
   A. 160°         C. 100°
   B. 120°         D. 80°

   1. _____

2. If $m\angle 6 = 80°$, find $m\angle 3$.
   F. 100°     G. 80°     H. 120°     J. 160°

   2. _____

3. Angles $L$ and $M$ are supplementary. Find $m\angle L$ if $m\angle M = 120°$.
   A. 30°     B. 50°     C. 60°     D. 120°

   3. _____

4. If $\triangle ABC \cong \triangle XZY$, which segment is congruent to $\overline{BC}$?
   F. $\overline{XY}$     G. $\overline{XZ}$     H. $\overline{ZY}$     J. $\overline{AB}$

   4. _____

5. Identify the transformation at the right.
   A. translation
   B. reflection
   C. rotation
   D. cannot tell

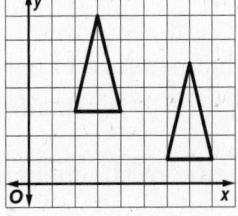

   5. _____

6. Quadrilateral $ABCD$ is shown at the right. Find the value of $x$.
   F. 55         H. 170
   G. 220        J. 85

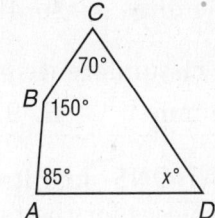

   6. _____

7. Which quadrilateral has four congruent angles?
   A. parallelogram         C. rectangle
   B. trapezoid             D. rhombus

   7. _____

**For Questions 8–11, find the area of each figure shown or described.**

8. parallelogram: base, 6 cm; height, 9 cm
   F. 27 cm²     G. 169.6 cm²     H. 54 cm²     J. 84.8 cm²

   8. _____

9.

   A. 339.1 m²     C. 54 m²
   B. 24 m²        D. 108 m²

   9. _____

10. trapezoid: height, 8 in.; bases, 3 in., 5 in.
    F. 48 in²     G. 16 in²     H. 120 in²     J. 32 in²

    10. _____

11. circle: diameter, 14 in.
    A. 615.8 in²     B. 153.9 in²     C. 43.9 in²     D. 22 in²

    11. _____

Assessment

**For Questions 12 and 13, find the area of each figure.**

**12.**

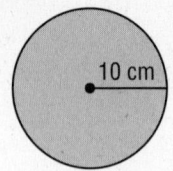

F. 314.2 cm$^2$          H. 62.8 cm$^2$

G. 31.4 cm$^2$           J. 628 cm$^2$                              12. _____

**13.**

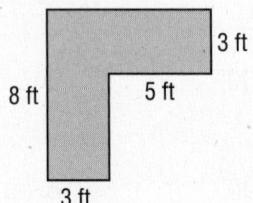

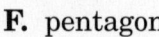

A. 39 ft$^2$          C. 40 ft$^2$

B. 48 ft$^2$          D. 120 ft$^2$                              13. _____

**14.** Classify the polygon shown at the right.

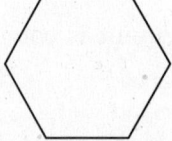

    F. pentagon          H. hexagon

    G. octagon           J. heptagon                              14. _____

**15.** Choose the measure of each interior angle of a regular pentagon.

    A. 130°          B. 50°          C. 108°          D. 72°          15. _____

**16.** Find the sum of the measures of the interior angles of a polygon having six sides.

    F. 720°          G. 1080°          H. 700°          J. 600°          16. _____

**17.** Find the circumference of a circle with a radius of 3 millimeters.

    A. 28.26 mm          B. 9.42 mm          C. 18.85 mm          D. 12.56 mm          17. _____

**18. DECORATIONS** Juanita ordered orchids in 8-inch diameter ceramic pots as centerpieces for the tables at the school spring dance. She wants to put a strip of foil around the rim of each pot. What length of foil does Juanita need for each pot?

    F. 12.57 in.          G. 25.13 in.          H. 50.27 in.          J. 201.96 in.          18. _____

**19.** If $\triangle LMN \cong \triangle VWX$, which angle is congruent to $\angle W$?

    A. $\angle L$          B. $\angle V$          C. $\angle M$          D. $\angle N$          19. _____

**20.** A figure has vertices $A(4, 1)$, $B(2, 3)$, $C(0, 5)$, and $D(3, 4)$. After a translation of 3 units to the right, which point is *not* a vertex of the translated image?

    F. (7, 1)          G. (5, 3)          H. (6, 4)          J. (0, 8)          20. _____

**Bonus  BEACHBALL** The circumference of a beachball is 56.52 inches. Find the diameter of the beachball.          B: _____

**10** **Chapter 10 Test, Form 2A**

SCORE _____

*Write the letter for the correct answer in the blank at the right of each question.*

In the figure at the right, *r* ∥ *s* and *t* is a transversal.
If *m*∠3 = 35°, find the measure of each angle. Use
the figure for Questions 1 and 2.

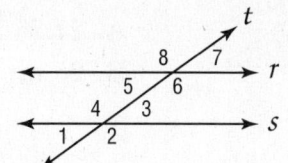

1. ∠1
   **A.** 35°          **C.** 145°
   **B.** 45°          **D.** 180°                                    1. _____

2. ∠8
   **F.** 35°       **G.** 90°       **H.** 145°       **J.** 165°       2. _____

3. Angles *L* and *M* are complementary. If *m*∠*L* = (*x* + 2)° and *m*∠*M* = (*x* − 6)°,
   what is the value of *x*?
   **A.** 35          **B.** 47          **C.** 92          **D.** 139          3. _____

4. If △*ABC* ≅ △*KLM*, which angle is congruent to ∠*K*?
   **F.** ∠*C*       **G.** ∠*A*       **H.** ∠*L*       **J.** ∠*B*          4. _____

5. Suppose the figure shown at the right is translated
   4 units to the right and 3 units down. Which point
   is *not* a vertex of the translated image?
   **A.** (1, −3)       **C.** (3, 1)
   **B.** (1, 0)        **D.** (−4, 0)                                5. _____

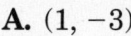

6. Use the figure at the right to find the value of *x*.
   **F.** 82°       **H.** 90°
   **G.** 152°       **J.** 103°                                      6. _____

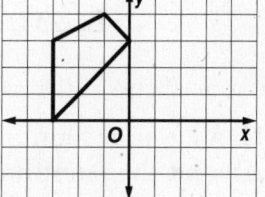
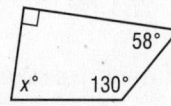

7. Which quadrilateral has exactly one pair of parallel sides?
   **A.** rectangle       **B.** trapezoid       **C.** rhombus       **D.** square       7. _____

8. Classify the quadrilateral at the right using the name
   that best describes it.
   **F.** rectangle       **H.** parallelogram
   **G.** rhombus         **J.** quadrilateral                        8. _____

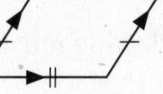

9. **POSTERS** Members of the pep club want to put crepe paper streamers
   around the edges of circular posters. What length of crepe paper is needed
   to go around a poster with a radius of 15 inches?
   **A.** 94.2 in.       **B.** 706.5 in.       **C.** 47.1 in.       **D.** 188.4 in.       9. _____

10. Find the circumference of a circle with a diameter of 14 inches.
    **F.** 22 in.       **G.** 153.9 in.       **H.** 44 in.       **J.** 615.4 in.       10. _____

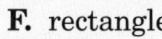

Assessment

**10** **Chapter 10 Test, Form 2A** *(continued)*

**For Questions 11–15, find the area of each figure shown or described.**

**11.**

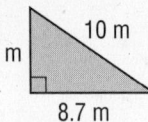

10 m
5 m
8.7 m

**A.** 21.75 m²    **C.** 37.5 m²

**B.** 25 m²    **D.** 50 m²

11. _____

**12.**

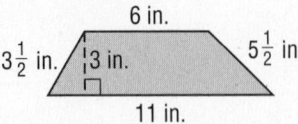

6 in.
$3\frac{1}{2}$ in.   3 in.   $5\frac{1}{2}$ in.
11 in.

**F.** 51 in²    **H.** $25\frac{1}{2}$ in²

**G.** 27 in²    **J.** $13\frac{1}{2}$ in²

12. _____

**13.** parallelogram: base, 18 cm; height, 25 cm

**A.** 450 cm²    **B.** 225 cm²    **C.** 900 cm²    **D.** 648 cm²

13. _____

**14.** circle: radius, 7 in.

**F.** 1230.9 in²    **G.** 307.7 in²    **H.** 615.4 in²    **J.** 153.9 in²

14. _____

**15.**

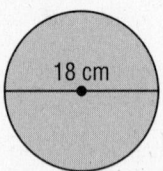

18 cm

**A.** 508.7 cm²    **C.** 1017.4 cm²

**B.** 254.5 cm²    **D.** 113.0 cm²

15. _____

**16. GARDEN** A circular fountain has a diameter of 8 feet. A flower garden is planted around the fountain. If the garden extends 12 feet beyond the fountain, what is the area of the flower garden?

**F.** 1056 ft²    **G.** 754 ft²    **H.** 452 ft²    **J.** 402 ft²

16. _____

**17.** Choose the measure of each interior angle of a regular decagon.

**A.** 10°    **B.** 170°    **C.** 36°    **D.** 144°

17. _____

**18.** Find the sum of the measures of the interior angles of a polygon having nine sides.

**F.** 1620°    **G.** 1800°    **H.** 1980°    **J.** 1260°

18. _____

**19.** Which of the following must be true if $\triangle BCD \cong \triangle GHF$?

**A.** $\angle B \cong \angle F$      **C.** $\overline{BC} \cong \overline{HF}$

**B.** $\angle CDB \cong \angle HFG$      **D.** $\overline{BD} \cong \overline{HG}$

19. _____

**20.** A figure has vertices $A(-4, 0)$, $B(3, 5)$, $C(0, -2)$, and $D(-3, -2)$. After a translation of 3 units to the left and 4 units down, which point is *not* a vertex of the translated image?

**F.** $(-3, -6)$    **G.** $(-6, -6)$    **H.** $(0, 1)$    **J.** $(-1, 2)$

20. _____

**Bonus** The ratio of the sides of 2 squares is 3:1. What is the ratio of their areas?

**B:** _____

**10** **Chapter 10 Test, Form 2B** SCORE _____

*Write the letter for the correct answer in the blank at the right of each question.*

In the figure at the right, $r \parallel s$ and $t$ is a transversal. If $m\angle 4 = 145°$, find the measure of each angle. Use the figure for Questions 1 and 2.

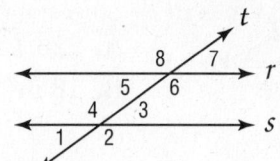

1. $\angle 2$
   - **A.** 35°
   - **B.** 145°
   - **C.** 45°
   - **D.** 180°

   1. _____

2. $\angle 7$
   - **F.** 35°
   - **G.** 45°
   - **H.** 90°
   - **J.** 145°

   2. _____

3. Angles $L$ and $M$ are supplementary. If $m\angle L = (x + 2)°$ and $m\angle M = (x - 6)°$, what is the value of $x$?
   - **A.** 35
   - **B.** 47
   - **C.** 92
   - **D.** 139

   3. _____

4. If $\triangle LMN \cong \triangle VWX$, which angle is congruent to $\angle N$?
   - **F.** $\angle W$
   - **G.** $\angle V$
   - **H.** $\angle M$
   - **J.** $\angle X$

   4. _____

5. Suppose the figure shown is translated 3 units to the right and 4 units down. Which point is *not* a vertex of the translated image?
   - **A.** $(0, -4)$
   - **B.** $(-4, 0)$
   - **C.** $(0, -1)$
   - **D.** $(2, 0)$

   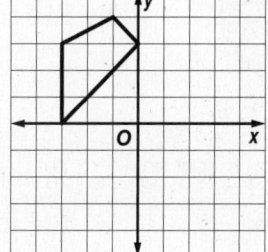

   5. _____

6. Use the figure at the right to find the value of $x$.
   - **F.** 87°
   - **G.** 97°
   - **H.** 90°
   - **J.** 77°

   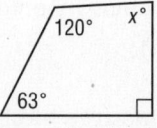

   6. _____

7. Which quadrilateral does *not* have two pairs of parallel sides?
   - **A.** trapezoid
   - **B.** rectangle
   - **C.** rhombus
   - **D.** square

   7. _____

8. Classify the quadrilateral at the right using the name that best describes it.
   - **F.** square
   - **G.** parallelogram
   - **H.** rhombus
   - **J.** quadrilateral

   8. _____

9. **FENCE** Desiree wants to place a wire fence around the base of an apple tree. The tree base and mulch area around it is shaped like a circle that has a radius of 14 inches. What length of fencing does Desiree need?
   - **A.** 43.98 in.
   - **B.** 615.75 in.
   - **C.** 87.96 in.
   - **D.** 175.93 in.

   9. _____

10. Find the circumference of a circle with diameter 15 inches.
    - **F.** 23.6 in.
    - **G.** 47.1 in.
    - **H.** 176.7 in.
    - **J.** 706.9 in.

    10. _____

Assessment

**For Questions 11–15, find the area of each figure shown or described.**

**11.**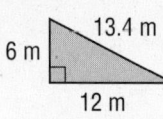

**A.** 226.1 m$^2$      **C.** 72 m$^2$

**B.** 18 m$^2$         **D.** 36 m$^2$

11. _____

**12.**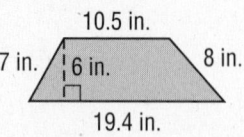

**F.** 66,112 in$^2$     **H.** 89.7 in$^2$

**G.** 13,612 in$^2$     **J.** 8113 in$^2$

12. _____

**13.** parallelogram: base, 15 cm; height, 21 cm

**A.** 157.5 cm$^2$    **B.** 989.1 cm$^2$    **C.** 315 cm$^2$    **D.** 105 cm$^2$

13. _____

**14.** circle: diameter, 18 in.

**F.** 113.1 in$^2$    **G.** 254.5 in$^2$    **H.** 1017.9 in$^2$    **J.** 56.5 in$^2$

14. _____

**15.**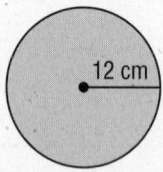

**A.** 452.4 cm$^2$      **C.** 113.1 cm$^2$

**B.** 144 cm$^2$        **D.** 75.4 cm$^2$

15. _____

**16. FRAMING** A mat forms a 3-inch wide border around a photograph. The mat fits in a 15-inch square frame. What is the area of the mat?

**F.** 225 in$^2$    **G.** 108 in$^2$    **H.** 180 in$^2$    **J.** 144 in$^2$

16. _____

**17.** Choose the measure of each interior angle of a regular octagon.

**A.** 60°    **B.** 120°    **C.** 45°    **D.** 135°

17. _____

**18.** Find the sum of the measures of the interior angles of a polygon having ten sides.

**F.** 900°    **G.** 2160°    **H.** 1440°    **J.** 1800°

18. _____

**19.** Which of the following must be true if $\triangle BCD \cong \triangle GEF$?

**A.** $\angle C \cong \angle F$                **C.** $\angle D \cong \angle G$

**B.** $\angle CDB \cong \angle EFG$            **D.** $\overline{DB} \cong \overline{GE}$

19. _____

**20.** A figure has vertices $A(-4, 0)$, $B(0, -2)$, $C(3, 5)$, and $D(-3, -2)$. After a translation of 3 units to the left and 4 units up, which point is *not* a vertex of the translated image?

**F.** $(-6, 2)$    **G.** $(0, 1)$    **H.** $(-3, 2)$    **J.** $(-7, 4)$

20. _____

**Bonus** A right triangle has a hypotenuse with length 13 in. and a leg with length 12 in. Find the area of the triangle.      **B:** _____

**10** **Chapter 10 Test, Form 2C**

**In the figure at the right, $\ell \parallel m$ and $t$ is a transversal. Use the figure for Questions 1 and 2.**

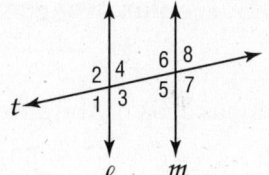

1. If $m\angle 1 = 78°$, find $m\angle 3$.

1. _____

2. If $m\angle 4 = 78°$, find $m\angle 5$.

2. _____

3. Find $m\angle A$ if $m\angle B = 38°$ and $\angle A$ and $\angle B$ are complementary.

3. _____

4. Find $m\angle 4$ if $m\angle 2 = 65°$ and $\angle 4$ and $\angle 2$ are vertical angles.

4. _____

5. If $\triangle ABC \cong \triangle XZY$, what segment is congruent to $\overline{ZY}$?

5. _____

6. **ORIGAMI** Alex is using origami to make a paper crane. In the process, he notices that $\triangle WXR \cong \triangle ZXY$. What is the length of $\overline{ZX}$ if $\overline{RX} = 10$ centimeters and $\overline{WX} = 12$ centimeters?

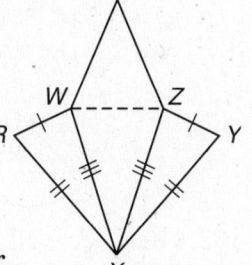

6. _____

7. Triangle $DFG$ has vertices $D(-2, 2)$, $F(2, 3)$, and $G(2, 0)$. Graph the image after a translation 2 units right and 4 units down.

7.

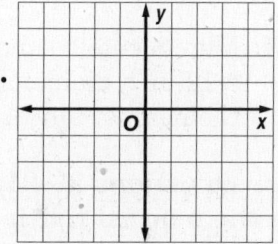

8. The vertices of a figure are $A(-3, -3)$, $B(-1, 1)$, $C(2, -1)$, and $D(3, -3)$. Graph the image of its reflection over the $y$-axis.

8.

**For Questions 9–11, find the area of each figure described. Round to the nearest tenth if necessary.**

9. parallelogram: base, $3\frac{1}{4}$ in.; height, $5\frac{1}{2}$ in.

9. _____

10. triangle: base, 12 m; height, 7.7 m

10. _____

11. circle: diameter, 22 cm

11. _____

12. Find the value of $x$. Then find the missing angle measures. Use the figure at the right.

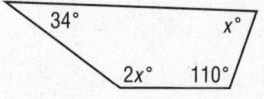

12. _____

13. Draw and name a quadrilateral that is equilateral but not equiangular.

13.

_____

**14.** What is the perimeter of a regular hexagon with sides 5.4 inches long?

14. _____

**15.** What is the sum of the measures of the interior angles of a pentagon?

15. _____

**16.** Find the measure of each interior angle of a 15-gon.

16. _____

**For Questions 17–20, find the circumference of each circle described or shown. Round to the nearest hundredth.**

**17.** The diameter is 6.5 centimeters.

17. _____

**18.** The radius is 7.8 inches.

18. _____

**19.**
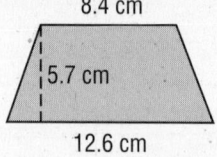
10 cm

19. _____

**20.**
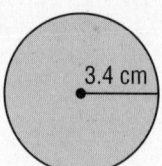
30 ft

20. _____

**21.** Miguel cuts a square with 5-inch sides out of a circle with a 12-inch diameter. Find the area of the remaining piece to the nearest tenth.

21. _____

**For Questions 22–24, find the area of each figure. Round to the nearest tenth if necessary.**

**22.**
8.4 cm
5.7 cm
12.6 cm

22. _____

**23.**
3.4 cm

23. _____

**24.**
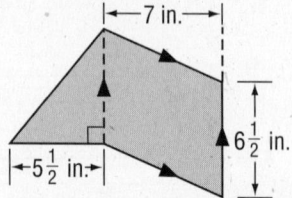
|←—7 in.—→|
6$\frac{1}{2}$ in.
|←5$\frac{1}{2}$ in.→|

24. _____

**25.** Find the base of a parallelogram with a height of 9.7 meters and an area of 58.2 square meters.

25. _____

**Bonus  COINS** The circumference of a U.S. quarter which was first issued in 1932 is about 76.18 millimeters. Find the diameter of a quarter.

B: _____

## 10 Chapter 10 Test, Form 2D

SCORE _____

**In the figure at the right, $\ell \parallel m$ and $a$ is a transversal. Use the figure for Questions 1 and 2.**

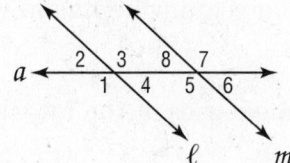

1. If $m\angle 4 = 42°$, find $m\angle 7$.

1. _____

2. If $m\angle 6 = 42°$, find $m\angle 8$.

2. _____

3. Find $m\angle A$ if $m\angle B = 12°$ and $\angle A$ and $\angle B$ are supplementary.

3. _____

4. Find $m\angle 2$ if $m\angle 1 = 87°$ and $\angle 2$ and $\angle 1$ are vertical angles.

4. _____

5. If $\triangle XYZ \cong \triangle BCD$, which segment is congruent to $\overline{CD}$?

5. _____

6. **ORIGAMI** Sean is using origami to make a paper crane. In the process, he notices that $\triangle WXR \cong \triangle ZXY$. What is the length of $\overline{ZX}$ if $\overline{RX} = 9$ centimeters and $\overline{WX} = 11$ centimeters?

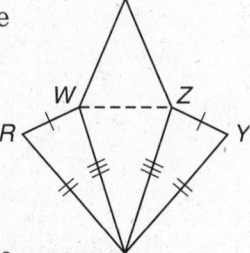

6. _____

7. Triangle $DFG$ has vertices $D(-3, 1)$, $F(-1, 2)$, and $G(-2, -2)$. Graph the image after a translation 2 units right and 2 units up.

7. _____

8. The vertices of a figure are $A(-3, 2)$, $B(-4, -1)$, $C(2, 1)$, and $D(0, -2)$. Graph the image of its reflection over the $x$-axis.

8. _____

**For Questions 9–11, find the area of each figure described. Round to the nearest tenth if necessary.**

9. parallelogram: base, $4\frac{1}{2}$ ft; height, $6\frac{1}{4}$ ft

9. _____

10. triangle: base, 14 m; height, 7.8 m

10. _____

11. circle: diameter, 24 cm

11. _____

12. Find the value of $x$. Then find the missing angle measures. Use the figure at the right.

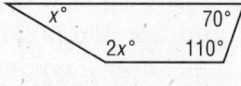

12. _____

13. Draw and name a quadrilateral that is equiangular but not equilateral.

13. _____

Assessment

**14.** What is the perimeter of a regular heptagon with sides 5.4 centimeters long?

14. _____

**15.** What is the sum of the measures of the interior angles of a hexagon?

15. _____

**16.** Find the measure of each interior angle of a 16-gon.

16. _____

**For Questions 17–20, find the circumference of each circle described or shown. Round to the nearest hundredth.**

**17.** The diameter is 12.5 centimeters.

17. _____

**18.** The radius is 4.9 inches.

18. _____

**19.**
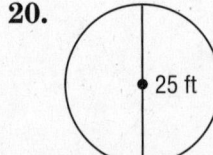
13 cm

19. _____

**20.**
25 ft

20. _____

**21.** Krista cuts a square with 4-inch sides out of a circle with a 9-inch diameter. Find the area of the remaining piece to the nearest tenth.

21. _____

**For Questions 22–24, find the area of each figure to the nearest tenth.**

**22.**
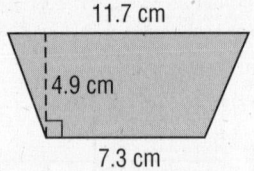
11.7 cm
4.9 cm
7.3 cm

**23.**
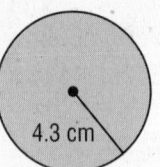
4.3 cm

22. _____

23. _____

**24.**
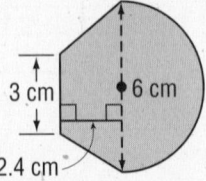
3 cm   6 cm
2.4 cm

24. _____

**25.** Find the base of a parallelogram with a height of 10.8 meters and an area of 75.6 square meters.

25. _____

**Bonus** **COINS** The diameter of the 2000 U.S. golden dollar depicting Sacagawea and her son is 26.5 millimeters. What is the circumference of the golden dollar? Round to the nearest tenth.

B: _____

# 10  Chapter 10 Test, Form 3

**In the figure at the right, $p \parallel q$ and $t$ is a transversal. Find the value of $x$ for Questions 1 and 2.**

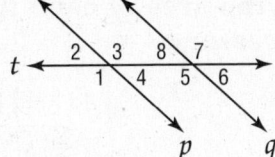

1. $m\angle 6 = (3x - 13)°$ and $m\angle 8 = (2x + 5)°$

1. _____

2. $m\angle 2 = (20x - 1)°$ and $m\angle 3 = (4x + 13)°$

2. _____

3. **ALGEBRA** If the measure of the supplement of an angle is 10° more than five times the measure of the complement, what is the measure of the angle?

3. _____

**Use the congruent triangles shown for Questions 4 and 5.**

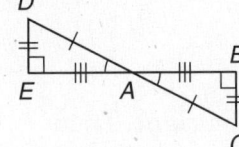

4. $\triangle BAC \cong \triangle \underline{\ ?\ }$

4. _____

5. If $AE = 3x + 2$, $AD = 4x - 7$, and $AC = 2x + 9$, what is the value of $x$?

5. _____

6. Find the coordinates of the vertices of the figure shown after a reflection over the $x$-axis. Then graph the reflection image.

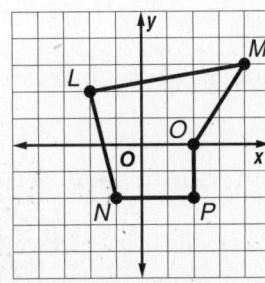

6. _____

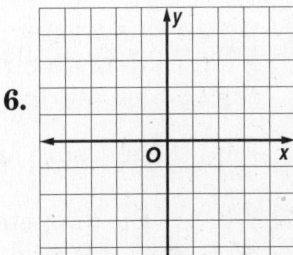

7. The vertices of a figure are $W(-1, 4)$, $X(-1, 1)$, $Y(-5, 1)$. Graph the image after a reflection over the $y$-axis and a rotation of 90° clockwise.

7.

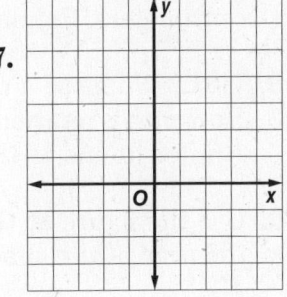

8. Use the figure at the right to find the value of $x$.

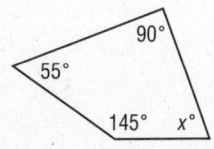

8. _____

9. Tell whether the statement is *sometimes, always,* or *never* true. Explain. A rhombus is a rectangle.

9. _____

Assessment

**For Questions 10–13, find the area of each figure. Round to the nearest tenth if necessary.**

10.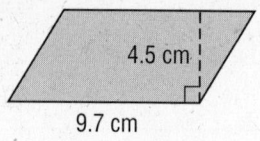

11.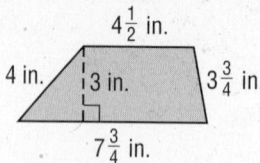

10. _____

11. _____

12.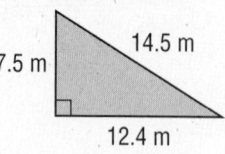

13.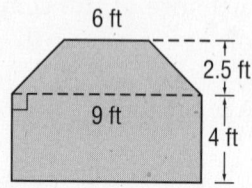

12. _____

13. _____

14. Classify the polygon at the right. Then determine whether it appears to be regular or not regular.

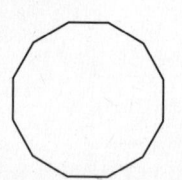

14. _____

15. Find the sum of the measures of the interior angles of a 21-gon.

15. _____

16. Find the measure of an interior angle of a regular 30-gon.

16. _____

17. What is the diameter of a circle if its circumference is 30.5 inches? Round to the nearest tenth.

17. _____

18. Find the radius of a circle if its area is 201 square centimeters. Round to the nearest tenth.

18. _____

19. **TIRES** Suppose a car tire has a diameter of 26 inches. How many rotations will the tire make if the car travels 1 mile? Round to the nearest whole rotation.

19. _____

20. Use the figure at the right to find the area of the shaded region.

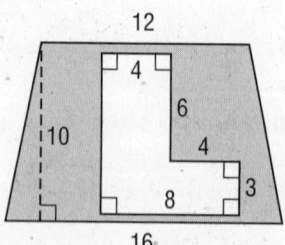

20. _____

**Bonus** The height of a triangle is one-half the length of the base of the triangle. Write an equation to find the area of the triangle in terms of the height, $h$.

B: _____

**10** **Chapter 10 Extended-Response Test**

Demonstrate your knowledge by giving a clear, concise solution to each problem. Be sure to include all relevant drawings and justify your answers. You may show your solution in more than one way or investigate beyond the requirements of the problem.

**Use the figure at the right for Questions 1 and 2.**

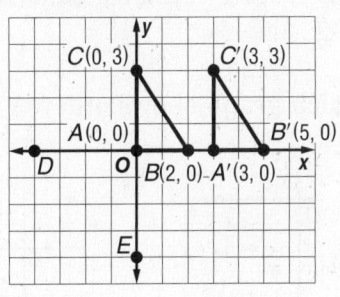

1. Computer graphics designers use transformations to create animation on the computer. When they do their programming, they actually use coordinates as you have done in this chapter. A triangle appears to be moving back and forth when the computer alternates rapidly between a screen showing △ABC and △A'B'C'.

   a. What kind of transformation of △ABC results in △A'B'C'? How do you know? Be as specific as possible.

   b. Is △ABC ≅ △A'B'C'? Why or why not?

   c. Explain how you could create an animation of a child on a swing using transformations.

   d. Draw a diagram on a coordinate grid showing your image and pre-image for the animation of the child.

2. Find an example of each of the following in the figure, if possible. Explain why you are sure that you are right.

   a. supplementary angles

   b. complementary angles

   c. vertical angles

   d. perpendicular lines

3. Make up an irregular figure consisting of at least three of the following figures or their parts: triangle, trapezoid, parallelogram, and circle. Label your drawing with measurements so that a classmate would have enough information to find its area.

4. a. What can you determine about the measures of interior angles of a non-regular polygon?

   b. Explain why you can find the measure of an interior angle of a regular polygon but you cannot find the measure of the interior angle of a non-regular polygon.

## 10 Standardized Test Practice

SCORE _____

*(Chapters 1-3)*

---

### Part 1: Multiple Choice

**Instructions:** Fill in the appropriate circle for the best answer.

---

**1.** Which value satisfies $5a + 13 = 43$? (Lesson 1–5)

   **A** 4       **B** 5       **C** 6       **D** 7

                                              **1.** Ⓐ Ⓑ Ⓒ Ⓓ

**2.** Which graph shows ordered pairs for the equation $x + y = -4$? (Lesson 2–6)

**F** 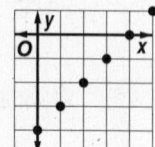   **G** 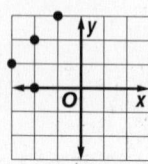   **H** 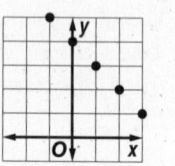   **J**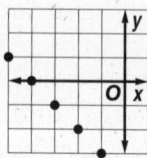

                                              **2.** Ⓕ Ⓖ Ⓗ Ⓙ

**3.** Which expression is equivalent to $(-5 + y)6$? (Lesson 3–1)

   **A** $y - 30$    **B** $6y - 30$    **C** $6y - 5$    **D** $30 - 6y$

                                              **3.** Ⓐ Ⓑ Ⓒ Ⓓ

**4.** Find the prime factorization of 120. (Lesson 4–2)

   **F** $2^3 \cdot 3 \cdot 5$    **G** $2^2 \cdot 3^2 \cdot 5$    **H** $8 \cdot 15$    **J** $10 \cdot 12$

                                              **4.** Ⓕ Ⓖ Ⓗ Ⓙ

**5.** What is the scale in a scale drawing where 2 inches is 6 feet? (Lesson 6–4)

   **A** $\dfrac{1}{6}$    **B** $\dfrac{1}{3}$    **C** $\dfrac{1}{2}$    **D** $\dfrac{3}{1}$

                                              **5.** Ⓐ Ⓑ Ⓒ Ⓓ

**6.** Solve the inequality $x - \dfrac{3}{5} > 7$. (Lesson 8–4)

   **F** $x > 7\dfrac{3}{5}$    **G** $x < 7\dfrac{3}{5}$    **H** $x > 6\dfrac{2}{5}$    **J** $x < 6\dfrac{2}{5}$

                                              **6.** Ⓕ Ⓖ Ⓗ Ⓙ

**7.** Which of the following relations is a function? (Lesson 7–1)

   **A** $\{(-2, 0), (-2, -2), (-1, 1)\}$

   **B** $\{(-3, 9), (2, 0), (-1, 4), (-3, 5)\}$

   **C** $\{(-1, 0), (2, -2), (1, 0)\}$

   **D** $\{(3, 5), (4, 0), (4, -4), (-3, -8)\}$

                                              **7.** Ⓐ Ⓑ Ⓒ Ⓓ

**8.** Give the slope of the line $6x + 3y = 18$. (Lesson 7–6)

   **F** 6    **G** $\dfrac{1}{2}$    **H** $-2$    **J** $-6$

                                              **8.** Ⓕ Ⓖ Ⓗ Ⓙ

**9.** Which of the following is a solution to the linear equation $4x - 2y = 6$? (Lesson 7–2)

   **A** $(0, 32)$    **B** $(-3, 0)$    **C** $(1, 1)$    **D** $(4, 5)$

                                              **9.** Ⓐ Ⓑ Ⓒ Ⓓ

**10.** Which statement is *not* true? (Lesson 9–1)

   **F** $6 < \sqrt{48} < 7$         **H** $-5 < -\sqrt{21} < -4$

   **G** $8 > \sqrt{84} > 9$         **J** $-7 > -\sqrt{37} > -6$

                                              **10.** Ⓕ Ⓖ Ⓗ Ⓙ

# 10 Standardized Test Practice *(continued)*

11. Which statement is true? (Lesson 9–2)
    - **A** All integers are rational numbers.
    - **B** Every whole number is a natural number.
    - **C** No real number is an irrational number.
    - **D** Some rational numbers are irrational.

    11. Ⓐ Ⓑ Ⓒ Ⓓ

12. Classify an angle with measure 34°. (Lesson 9–3)
    - **F** acute
    - **G** obtuse
    - **H** right
    - **J** straight

    12. Ⓕ Ⓖ Ⓗ Ⓙ

13. Angles $A$ and $B$ are supplementary and $m\angle A = 26°$.
    Find $m\angle B$. (Lesson 10–1)
    - **A** 164°
    - **B** 154°
    - **C** 64°
    - **D** 26°

    13. Ⓐ Ⓑ Ⓒ Ⓓ

14. If $\triangle ABC \cong \triangle DEF$, then which of the following is *not* necessarily true? (Lesson 10–2)
    - **F** $\overline{AC} \cong \overline{DF}$
    - **G** $\overline{AB} \cong \overline{DE}$
    - **H** $\overline{BC} \cong \overline{DE}$
    - **J** $\overline{CB} \cong \overline{FE}$

    14. Ⓕ Ⓖ Ⓗ Ⓙ

15. Find the area of a circle with a diameter of 10 inches. (Lesson 10–7)
    - **A** 31.4 in²
    - **B** 39.25 in²
    - **C** 78.5 in²
    - **D** 314 in²

    15. Ⓐ Ⓑ Ⓒ Ⓓ

16. Solve $-15 \le 9 - 3y$. (Lesson 8–4)
    - **F** $y = 8$
    - **G** $y \le -8$
    - **H** $y \le 8$
    - **J** $y \ge 8$

    16. Ⓕ Ⓖ Ⓗ Ⓙ

17. Find the area of a parallelogram with a base of 18 centimeters and a height of 10 centimeters. (Lesson 10–6)
    - **A** 28 cm²
    - **B** 56 cm²
    - **C** 180 cm²
    - **D** 1800 cm²

    17. Ⓐ Ⓑ Ⓒ Ⓓ

## Part 2: Griddable

**Instructions:** Enter your answer by writing each digit of the answer in a column box and then shading in the appropriate circle that corresponds to that entry.

18. Evaluate $3n^7$, if $n = 2$.
    (Lesson 4–1)

19. Find the sum of the measures of the interior angles of a 40-sided polygon.
    (Lesson 10–5)

Assessment

# 10 Standardized Test Practice *(continued)*

| Part 3: Short Response |
|---|
| **Instructions:** Write your answer in the blank at the right of each question. |

**20.** Find the 10th term of the sequence 5, 8, 11, 14, ... . (Lesson 3–7)   20. _____

**21.** Express $\frac{1}{6}$ as a decimal. (Lesson 5–1)   21. _____

**22.** State whether $\frac{33}{x} < 11$ is *true* or *false* for $x = 3$. (Lesson 8–3)   22. _____

**23.** Write an equation in slope-intercept form for the line passing through the points $A(-4, 1)$ and $B(0, 5)$. (Lesson 7–7)   23. _____

**24.** Find the distance between the points $F(-6, 5)$ and $G(4, -7)$. Round to the nearest tenth. (Lesson 9–5)   24. _____

**For Questions 25 and 26, use the table.** (Lesson 7–8)

| x | −3 | −2 | 0 | 1 | 2 | 3 | 4 | 5 |
|---|---|---|---|---|---|---|---|---|
| y | 0 | 10 | 20 | 26 | 35 | 38 | 46 | 50 |

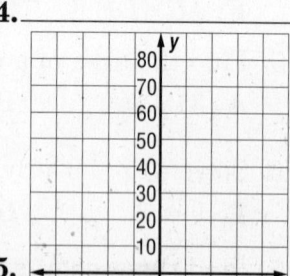

**25.** Make a scatter plot and draw a best-fit line for the data.   25.

**26.** Use the best-fit line to predict $y$ when $x = -1$.   26. _____

**27.** Angles $X$ and $Y$ are supplementary. Find the measure of angle $Y$ if the measure of angle $X$ is 25°. (Lesson 10–1)   27. _____

**28.** Find the area of a parallelogram with a length of 12 centimeters and a height of 15 centimeters. (Lesson 10–6)   28. _____

**29.** Find the sum of the measures of the interior angles of a 50-sided polygon. (Lesson 10–5)   29. _____

**30.** A load of bricks costs $0.30 per brick plus $24 delivery charge. Ross paid a total bill of $72 for bricks. (Lesson 3–6)

   **a.** Write an equation to find the number of bricks he bought.   30a. _____

   **b.** Solve the equation to determine how many bricks Ross bought.   30b. _____

   **c.** If Ross needs at most 150 bricks to make a patio, will he have enough?   30c. _____

# Answers (Anticipation Guide and Lesson 10-1)

## 10-1 Lesson Reading Guide

### Line and Angle Relationships

**Get Ready for the Lesson**

Read the introduction to Lesson 10-1 in your textbook. Write your answers below.

a. What do you notice about the lines coming into the satellite dish? **They are parallel.**

b. Trace the red lines onto a piece of paper. Find the measure of each angle. **See students' work.**

c. What do you notice about the measures of the angles? Which angles have the same measure? **There are just two different measures; Sample answer: The angles across from each other; the angles in the same position on each of the horizontal lines; the angles on opposite sides inside the horizontal lines; the angles on opposite sides above and below the parallel lines.**

**Read the Lesson**   1–9. See students' work.

Write a definition and give an example of each new vocabulary word or phrase.

| Vocabulary | Definition | Example |
|---|---|---|
| 1. parallel lines | | |
| 2. interior angles | | |
| 3. exterior angles | | |
| 4. corresponding angles | | |
| 5. vertical angles | | |
| 6. adjacent angles | | |
| 7. complementary angles | | |
| 8. supplementary angles | | |

**Remember What You Learned**

9. Draw two parallel, horizontal lines. Draw a third line (transversal) so it intersects the first pair. Label the eight angles. Identify two interior angles. (Interior angles are between the parallel lines.) Identify three angles that have the same measure. (Opposite and corresponding angles have the same measure.) If two angles are supplementary, and one of the angles measures 50°, what must the other angle measure? (Supplementary angles always equal 180°.) **130°**

---

## 10 Anticipation Guide

### Measuring Two-Dimensional Figures

**Step 1**   *Before you begin Chapter 10*

- Read each statement.
- Decide whether you Agree (A) or Disagree (D) with the statement.
- Write A or D in the first column OR if you are not sure whether you agree or disagree, write NS (Not Sure).

| STEP 1 A, D, or NS | Statement | Step 2 A or D |
|---|---|---|
| | 1. Parallel lines intersect in only one point. | D |
| | 2. When two parallel lines are intersected by a third line, eight angles are formed. | A |
| | 3. If the sum of the measures of two angles is 180°, the angles are complimentary. | D |
| | 4. Any two lines that intersect to form a right angle are perpendicular lines. | A |
| | 5. Two figures are congruent if they have the same size and shape. | A |
| | 6. To graph the ordered pair (3, 5) on coordinate plane, start at the origin and move three units up, then move five units to the right. | D |
| | 7. A quadrilateral is a closed figure with five sides. | D |
| | 8. If both pairs of opposite sides of a quadrilateral are parallel, then the quadrilateral is a parallelogram. | A |
| | 9. The area of a figure is the surface enclosed by that figure. | A |
| | 10. A trapezoid has two pairs of parallel sides. | D |
| | 11. All triangles are polygons. | A |
| | 12. The diameter of a circle is the distance from the center to any point on the circle. | D |

**Step 2**   *After you complete Chapter 10*

- Reread each statement and complete the last column by entering an A (Agree) or a D (Disagree).
- Did any of your opinions about the statements change from the first column?
- For those statements that you mark with a D, use a separate sheet of paper to explain why you disagree. Use examples, if possible.

# Answers (Lesson 10-1)

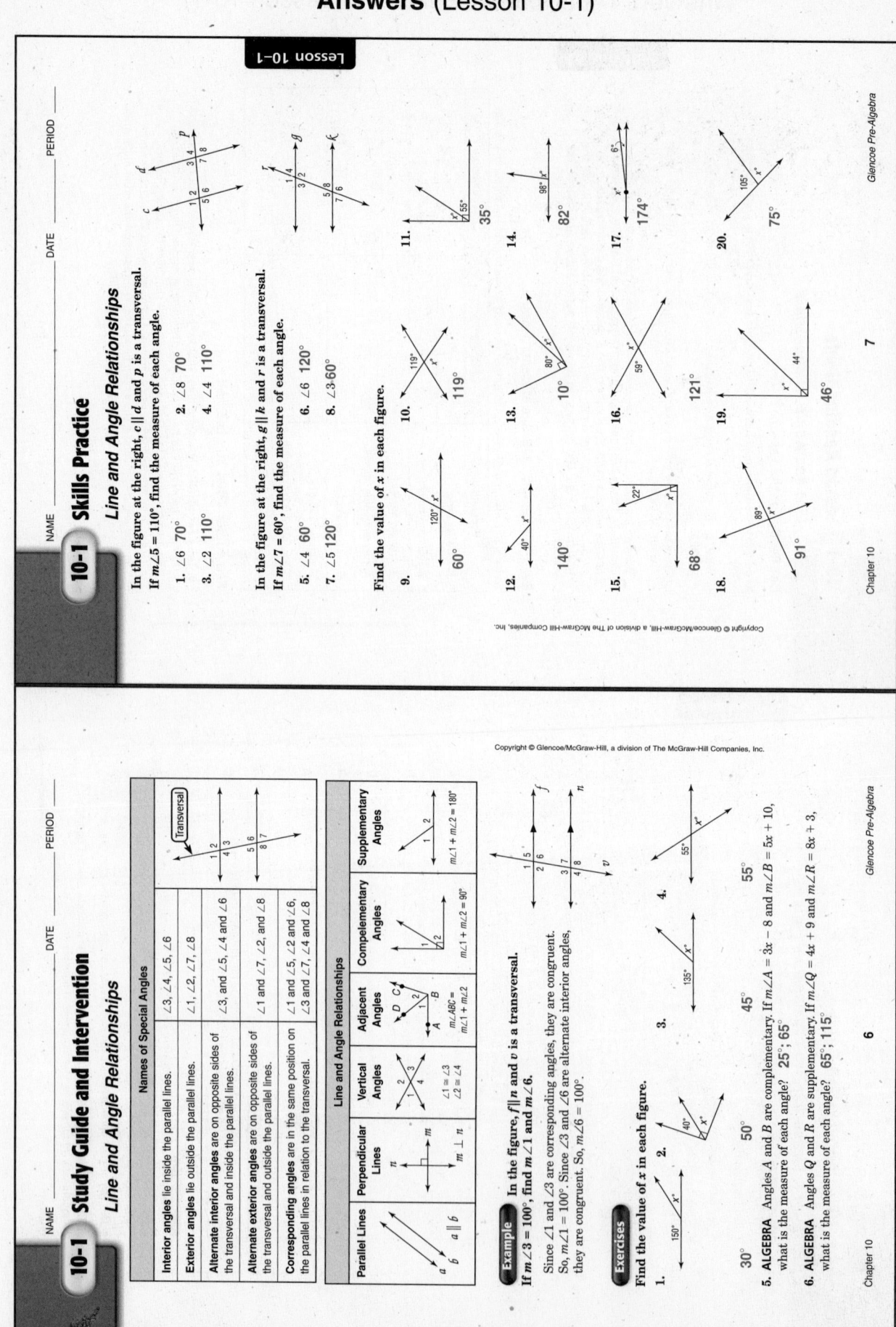

---

## Study Guide and Intervention (page 6)

NAME _____ DATE _____ PERIOD _____

### 10-1 Study Guide and Intervention

**Line and Angle Relationships**

#### Names of Special Angles

| | |
|---|---|
| Interior angles lie inside the parallel lines. | ∠3, ∠4, ∠5, ∠6 |
| Exterior angles lie outside the parallel lines. | ∠1, ∠2, ∠7, ∠8 |
| Alternate interior angles are on opposite sides of the transversal and inside the parallel lines. | ∠3, and ∠5, ∠4 and ∠6 |
| Alternate exterior angles are on opposite sides of the transversal and outside the parallel lines. | ∠1 and ∠7, ∠2, and ∠8 |
| Corresponding angles are in the same position on the parallel lines in relation to the transversal. | ∠1 and ∠5, ∠2 and ∠6, ∠3 and ∠7, ∠4 and ∠8 |

#### Line and Angle Relationships

| Parallel Lines | Perpendicular Lines | Vertical Angles | Adjacent Angles | Complementary Angles | Supplementary Angles |
|---|---|---|---|---|---|
| a ∥ b | m ⊥ n | ∠1 ≅ ∠3, ∠2 ≅ ∠4 | m∠ABC = m∠1 + m∠2 | m∠1 + m∠2 = 90° | m∠1 + m∠2 = 180° |

**Example** In the figure, f∥n and v is a transversal. If m∠3 = 100°, find m∠1 and m∠6.

Since ∠1 and ∠3 are corresponding angles, they are congruent. So, m∠1 = 100°. Since ∠3 and ∠6 are alternate interior angles, they are congruent. So, m∠6 = 100°.

### Exercises

**Find the value of x in each figure.**

1. 150° x°    **30°**
2. 40° x°    **50°**
3. 135° x°    **45°**
4. 55° x°    **55°**

5. **ALGEBRA** Angles A and B are complementary. If m∠A = 3x − 8 and m∠B = 5x + 10, what is the measure of each angle? **25°; 65°**

6. **ALGEBRA** Angles Q and R are supplementary. If m∠Q = 4x + 9 and m∠R = 8x + 3, what is the measure of each angle? **65°; 115°**

Chapter 10      6      Glencoe Pre-Algebra

---

## Skills Practice (page 7)

NAME _____ DATE _____ PERIOD _____

### 10-1 Skills Practice

**Line and Angle Relationships**

In the figure at the right, c ∥ d and p is a transversal. If m∠5 = 110°, find the measure of each angle.

1. ∠6   **70°**
2. ∠8   **70°**
3. ∠2   **110°**
4. ∠4   **110°**

In the figure at the right, g ∥ k and r is a transversal. If m∠7 = 60°, find the measure of each angle.

5. ∠4   **60°**
6. ∠6   **120°**
7. ∠5   **120°**
8. ∠3   **60°**

**Find the value of x in each figure.**

9. 120° x°    **60°**
10. 119° x°    **119°**
11. x° 55°    **35°**
12. 40° x°    **140°**
13. 80° x°    **10°**
14. 98° x°    **82°**
15. 22° x°    **68°**
16. 59° x°    **121°**
17. x° 6°    **174°**
18. 89° x°    **91°**
19. 44° x°    **46°**
20. 105° x°    **75°**

Chapter 10      7      Glencoe Pre-Algebra

NAME ______________ DATE ________ PERIOD ____

# 10-1 Practice

## Line and Angle Relationships

**In the figure at the right, $m \parallel n$ and $r$ is a transversal. If $m\angle 2 = 45°$, find the measure of each angle.**

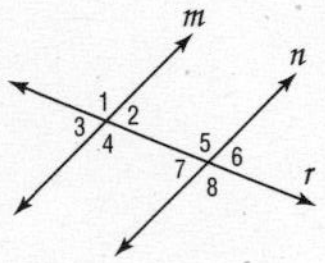


1. $\angle 4$ 135°
2. $\angle 5$ 135°
3. $\angle 7$ 45°
4. $\angle 8$ 135°
5. $\angle 6$ 45°
6. $\angle 3$ 45°

**In the figure at the right, $d \parallel e$ and $a$ is a transversal. If $m\angle 5 = 143°$, find the measure of each angle.**

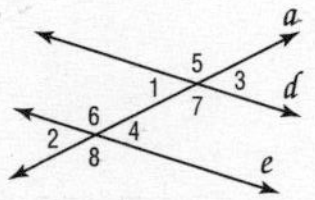


7. $\angle 7$ 143°
8. $\angle 6$ 143°
9. $\angle 4$ 37°
10. $\angle 2$ 37°
11. $\angle 1$ 37°
12. $\angle 8$ 143°

**Find the value of $x$ in each figure.**

13. 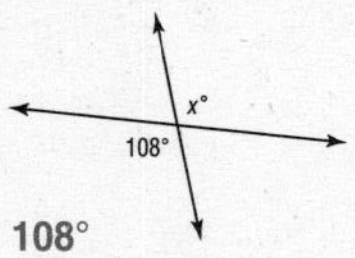

108°

14. 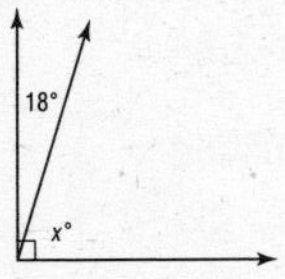

72°

15. 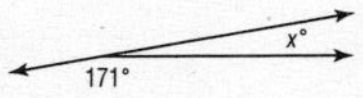

9°

16. 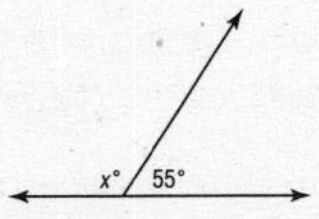

125°

17. 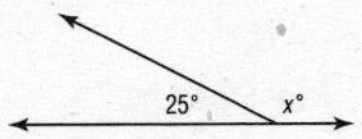

155°

18. 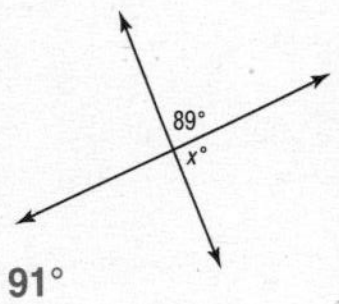

91°

19. Angles $Q$ and $R$ are complementary. Find $m\angle R$ if $m\angle Q = 24°$. 66°

20. Find $m\angle J$ if $m\angle K = 29°$ and $\angle J$ and $\angle K$ are supplementary. 151°

21. The measures of angles $A$ and $B$ are equal and complementary. What is the measure of each angle? 45°

22. **ALGEBRA** Angles $G$ and $H$ are complementary. If $m\angle G = 3x + 6$ and $m\angle H = 2x - 11$, what is the measure of each angle? $m\angle G = 63°$; $m\angle H = 27°$

Add
38 - 11 x = 19
27°
19
3
57
+6
63°





NAME ______________ DATE ________ PERIOD ____

# 10-1 Word Problem Practice

## Line and Angle Relationships

1. **PROPERTY LINES** The front and back property lines of Michaela's land are parallel lines. If the angle between the west side property line and back property line is 106°, what is the angle between the front property line and west side property line? 74°

2. **SCISSORS** Archie opened up a pair of scissor so that the angle between the blades is 38°. What is the angle between the handles?

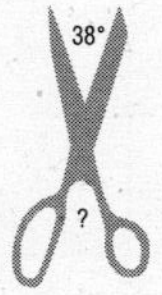


38°

3. **FENCING** The sections of fence in Sioban's yard have diagonal supports as shown. The top side of the diagonal support makes an angle of $x°$ with the fence slats. The bottom side makes an angle that is twice the measure of the top angle. Find the measures of both angles.

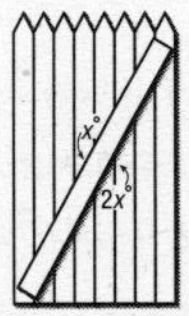


60°, 120°

4. **MAPS** In the following map, First Avenue, Second Avenue, and Third Avenue are parallel. Cross Street intersects all three avenues. First Avenue and Cross Street meet at a 25° angle. What angle does the intersection of Third Avenue and Cross Street make?

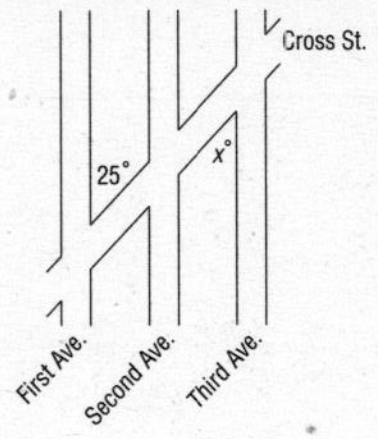


25°

**HIKING For Exercises 5 and 6, use the following information.**

Dave and Susie are walking on parallel trails in the woods. Dave's trail turns to the right 43° and meets up with Susie's trail.

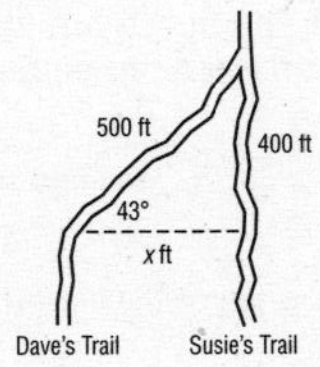


5. At what angle does Dave's trail meet Susie's trail? 47°

6. How far apart were Dave and Susie's trails originally? 300 ft

## Lesson 10-2

## 10-2 Lesson Reading Guide

### Congruent Triangles

**Get Ready for the Lesson**

**Read the introduction to Lesson 10-2 in your textbook. Write your answers below.**

a. Trace the triangles shown in your textbook onto a sheet of paper. Then label the triangles. **See students' work.**

b. Measure and then compare the lengths of the sides of the triangles. $AB = DF$, $AC = DE$, $BC = FE$

c. Measure the angles of each triangle. How do the angles compare? $m\angle A = m\angle D$, $m\angle B = m\angle F$, $m\angle C = m\angle E$

d. Make a conjecture about the triangles. Since the angles have the same measures and the sides have the same length, the triangles have the same size and shape.

**Read the Lesson   1–2. See students' work.**

Write a definition and give an example of each new vocabulary word or phrase.

| Vocabulary | Definition | Example |
|---|---|---|
| 1. congruent | | |
| 2. corresponding parts | | |

**Remember What You Learned**

3. Below are two congruent triangles. Name the corresponding parts and complete the congruence statement.

$\triangle GHF \cong \underline{\quad ? \quad} \triangle MNL$

**Sample answer:** $\angle G \cong \angle M$, $\angle H \cong \angle N$, $\angle L \cong \angle F$, $\overline{FG} \cong \overline{ML}$, $\overline{FH} \cong \overline{LN}$, $\overline{HG} \cong \overline{NM}$

---

## 10-1 Enrichment

### Geometric Proof

Use definitions and theorems for angle congruence to complete the proofs.

**Write the reason for each statement.**

1. Prove: $\angle 1 \cong \angle 3$

| Statement | Reason |
|---|---|
| a. $\angle 1$ and $\angle 3$ are vertical angles. | a. Given |
| b. $m\angle 1 + m\angle 2 = 180°$; $m\angle 3 + m\angle 2 = 180°$ | b. Def. Supp. $\angle$s |
| c. $m\angle 1 = 180° - m\angle 2$; $m\angle 3 = 180° - m\angle 2$ | c. Subtr. Prop. Equality |
| d. $m\angle 1 = m\angle 3$ | d. Substitution |
| e. $\angle 1 \cong \angle 3$ | e. Def. Congruent $\angle$s |

2. Prove: $m\angle 3 = m\angle 7$

| Statement | Reason |
|---|---|
| a. Line $p$ is parallel to line $q$. | a. Given |
| b. $m\angle 3 \cong m\angle 5$ | b. Alternate Interior $\angle$s |
| c. $m\angle 5 \cong m\angle 7$ | c. Vertical $\angle$s $\cong$ |
| d. $m\angle 3 \cong m\angle 7$ | d. Substitution |

# Answers (Lesson 10-2)

## 10-2 Skills Practice

### Congruent Triangles

For each pair of congruent triangles, name the corresponding parts. Then complete the congruence statement.

1. $\triangle KBS \cong \underline{\triangle QPN}$

$BK \cong \overline{PQ},\ SB \cong \overline{NP},\ KS \cong \overline{QN},$

$\angle S \cong \angle N,\ \angle B \cong \angle P,\ \angle K \cong \angle Q$

2. $\triangle ACB \cong \underline{\triangle ECD}$

$BC \cong \overline{DC},\ AC \cong \overline{EC},\ AB \cong \overline{ED},$

$\angle B \cong \angle D,\ \angle A \cong \angle E,\ \angle ACB \cong \angle ECD$

Complete each congruence statement if $\triangle MRU \cong \triangle ACF$.

3. $\angle R \cong \underline{?}\ \ \angle C$ 
4. $\overline{CA} \cong \underline{?}\ \ \overline{RM}$ 
5. $MU \cong \underline{?}\ \ \overline{AF}$ 
6. $\angle A \cong \underline{?}\ \ \angle M$

Complete each congruence statement if $\triangle GLE \cong \triangle SPT$.

7. $\overline{EL} \cong \underline{?}\ \ \overline{TP}$ 
8. $\angle S \cong \underline{?}\ \ \angle G$ 
9. $\angle E \cong \underline{?}\ \ \angle T$ 
10. $\overline{PS} \cong \underline{?}\ \ \overline{LG}$

Find the value of $x$ for each pair of congruent triangles.

11. **22** 
12. **31** 
13. **10**

**ARCHITECTURE** For Exercises 14 and 15, use the diagram of the Eiffel Tower truss at the right and the fact that $\triangle ACB \cong \triangle DFE$.

14. Find the distance between $A$ and $B$. **15 ft**

15. What is the measure of $\angle B$? **37°**

## 10-2 Study Guide and Intervention

### Congruent Triangles

**Corresponding Parts of Congruent Triangles**

**Words** Two triangles are **congruent** if they have the same size and shape.
If two triangles are congruent, their corresponding sides are congruent and their corresponding angles are congruent.

**Model**

Slash marks are used to indicate which sides are congruent.

Arcs are used to indicate which angles are congruent.

**Symbols** Congruent Angles: $\angle X \cong \angle P, \angle Y \cong \angle Q, \angle Z \cong \angle R$
Congruent Sides: $\overline{XY} \cong \overline{PQ}, \overline{YZ} \cong \overline{QR}, \overline{XZ} \cong \overline{PR}$

**Example** Name the corresponding parts in the congruent triangles shown. Then write a congruence statement.

Corresponding Angles
$\angle Q \cong \angle S, \angle R \cong \angle Z, \angle N \cong \angle V$
Corresponding Sides
$\overline{SZ} \cong \overline{QR}, \overline{ZV} \cong \overline{RN}, \overline{VS} \cong \overline{NQ}$
$\triangle NQR \cong \triangle VSZ$

**Exercises**

Complete each congruence statement if $\triangle DFH \cong \triangle PWZ$.

1. $\angle F \cong \underline{\angle W}$ 
2. $\angle P \cong \underline{\angle D}$ 
3. $\overline{DH} \cong \underline{\overline{PZ}}$ 
4. $\overline{ZW} \cong \underline{\overline{HF}}$

Find the value of $x$ for each pair of congruent triangles.

5. **24** 
6. **12** 
7. **8** 
8. **9**

# Answers (Lesson 10-2)

---

## 10-2 Practice

### Congruent Triangles

Complete the congruence statement if $\triangle CMH \cong \triangle PLF$ and $\triangle DNO \cong \triangle AET$.

1. $\angle M \cong$ __∠L__  2. $\overline{MC} \cong$ __LP__  3. $\overline{DN} \cong$ __AE__  4. $\angle A \cong$ __∠D__

5. $\overline{FL} \cong$ __HM__  6. $\angle C \cong$ __∠P__  7. $\overline{TE} \cong$ __ON__  8. $\angle O \cong$ __∠T__

Find the value of x for each pair of congruent triangles.

9. **16**  10. **11**  11. **10**

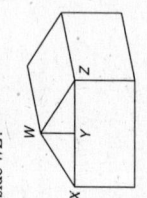

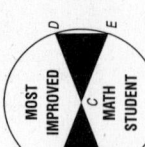

12. ALGEBRA If $\triangle DEC \cong \triangle PRM$, what is the value of x? **3**

13. ALGEBRA If $\triangle AHB \cong \triangle KJP$, what is the value of x? **2**

KALEIDOSCOPE For Exercises 14–19, use the kaleidoscope pattern at the right. Name a triangle that appears to be congruent to each triangle listed.

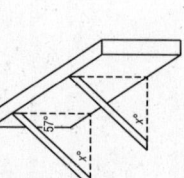

14. $\triangle GEH$  $\triangle GEF$
15. $\triangle FCH$  $\triangle HAF$
16. $\triangle DEC$  $\triangle DEA$
17. $\triangle ABD$  $\triangle CBD$
18. $\triangle HEF$  $\triangle HED$
19. $\triangle CBE$  $\triangle ABE$

For Exercises 14–19, sample answers are given.

---

## 10-2 Word Problem Practice

### Congruent Triangles

1. ROOFING The structure of a roof can be broken into congruent triangles. If side $\overline{WX}$ is 12 feet long, what is the length of side $\overline{WZ}$?

   **12 feet**

2. CONSTRUCTION Braces are often used to support walls during the construction of a house. If the two braces used in the following house are the same length and perpendicular to the ground, what is the measure of the angle x where the braces meet the ground?

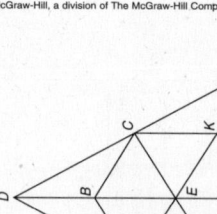

   **33°**

3. FLOWER BEDS Jane has two congruent flower beds in her backyard. The flower beds are triangular in shape. If the longest side of one flower bed is 12 feet, how long is the longest side of the other flower bed? **12 feet**

4. AWARDS The award for Most Improved Math Student in Mrs. Pike's classroom is a circle containing two congruent triangles connected at a vertex. What side in $\triangle ABC$ corresponds to $\overline{DE}$?

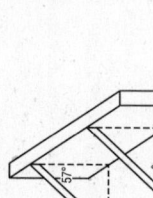

   $\overline{AB}$

KITES For Exercises 5 and 6, use the following information.

Joey's kite is made up of 4 congruent right triangles and 1 square as shown in the diagram below.

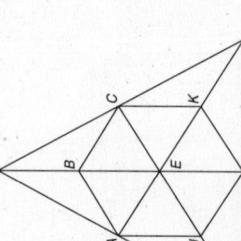

5. What are the three side lengths of each triangle? **5 cm, 12 cm, 13 cm**

6. What is the perimeter of Joey's kite? **52 cm**

---

# Answers (Lessons 10-2 and 10-3)

---

## Lesson 10-3

NAME _____ DATE _____ PERIOD _____

## 10-3 Lesson Reading Guide

### Transformations on the Coordinate Plane

**Get Ready for the Lesson**

Read the introduction to Lesson 10-3 in your textbook. Write your answers below.

a. Describe the motion involved in making a 180° turn on a skateboard. **Sample answer: The skateboard lands in the opposite direction from where it started.**

b. What type of motion does a scooter display when moving forward? **Sample answer: A scooter moves from one position to another position.**

**Read the Lesson**   1–5. **See students' work.**

Write a definition and give an example of each new vocabulary word or phrase.

| Vocabulary | Definition | Example |
|---|---|---|
| **1.** transformation | | |
| **2.** translation | | |
| **3.** reflection | | |
| **4.** line of symmetry | | |
| **5.** dilation | | |

**Remember What You Learned**

**6.** Complete the diagrams below by filling in each blank with one of the vocabulary words or phrases.

A movement of a geometric figure is called a __transformation__.

dilation

reflection

line of symmetry

translation

Chapter 10                                    17                        Glencoe Pre-Algebra

---

## Lesson 10-2

NAME _____ DATE _____ PERIOD _____

## 10-2 Enrichment

### Constructions: Congruent Triangles

Construct a triangle congruent to the given triangle using the **SSS rule.**
(Three sides of one triangle are congruent to three sides of another triangle.)

Given △ ABC          Step 1          Step 2          Step 3

Construct a triangle congruent to the given triangle using the **SAS rule.**
(Two sides and the included angle of one triangle are congruent to two sides and the included angle of another triangle.)

Given △ RST     Use ($\overline{RT}$, $\angle T$, $\overline{ST}$).
          Step 1          Step 2          Step 3

Construct a triangle congruent to the given triangle using the **ASA rule.**
(Two angles and the included side of one triangle are congruent to two angles and the included side of another triangle.)

Given △ DEF     Use ($\angle D$, $\overline{DE}$, $\angle E$).
          Step 1          Step 2          Step 3

Construct a triangle congruent to triangle **KJL.**
Use the rule and parts specified.

**1.** SSS; Use: $\overline{JL}$, $\overline{JK}$, $\overline{KL}$

**2.** SAS; Use: $\overline{JL}$, $\angle L$, $\overline{KL}$

**3.** ASA; Use: $\angle K$, $\overline{KL}$, $\angle L$

**As shown in the examples above.**

Chapter 10                                    16                        Glencoe Pre-Algebra

# Answers (Lesson 10-3)

---

NAME _____ DATE _____ PERIOD _____

## 10-3 Skills Practice

### Transformations on the Coordinate Plane

Find the coordinates of the vertices of each figure after the given translation. Then graph the translation image.

1. (5, 2)

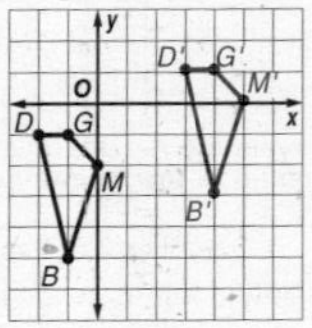

$D'(3, 1), G'(4, 1),$
$M'(5, 0), B'(4, -3)$

2. (-3, 4)

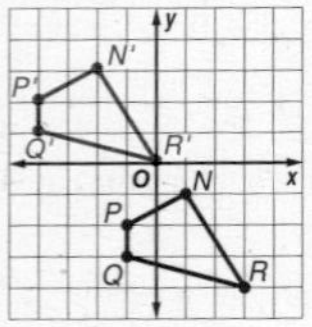

$P'(-4, 2), Q'(-4, 1),$
$R'(0, 0), N'(-2, 3)$

3. (-1, -5)

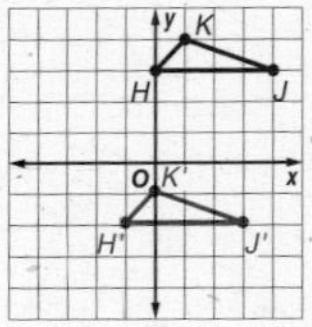

$H'(-1, -2), K'(0, -1),$
$J'(3, -2)$

Find the coordinates of the vertices of each figure after a reflection over the given axis. Then graph the reflection image.

4. y-axis

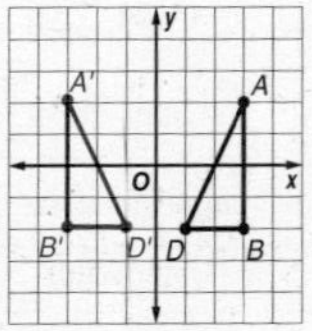

$A'(-3, 2), B'(-3, -2),$
$D'(-1, -2)$

5. x-axis

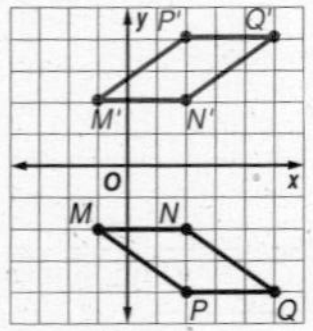

$M'(-1, 2), P'(2, 4),$
$Q'(5, 4), N'(2, 2)$

6. x-axis

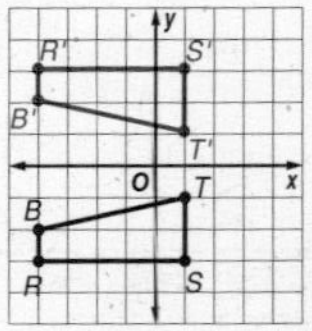

$B'(-4, 2), R'(-4, 3),$
$S'(1, 3), T'(1, 1)$

For Exercises 7–8, use the graph shown.

7. Graph the image of the figure after a dilation centered at the origin with a scale factor of 2.

8. Find the coordinates of the vertices after a dilation centered at the origin with a scale factor of $\frac{1}{2}$.

$M'\left(\frac{1}{2}, 1\right), N'(2, 1), Q'(1.5, 0), \text{ and } P'(0, 0)$

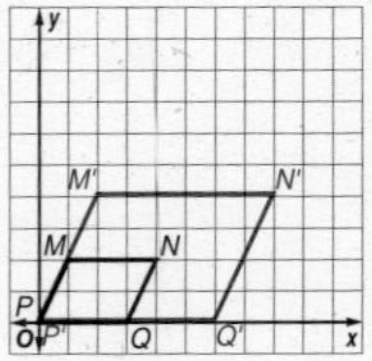

Chapter 10      19      *Glencoe Pre-Algebra*

---

NAME _____ DATE _____ PERIOD _____

## 10-3 Study Guide and Intervention

### Transformations on the Coordinate Plane

| Transformation | Movement | How To's |
|---|---|---|
| Translation | You slide a figure from one position to another without turning it. Every point of the original figure is moved the same distance and in the same direction. | To describe the translation using an ordered pair, add the coordinates of the ordered pair to the coordinates of the original point. |
| Reflection | You flip a figure over a **line of symmetry**. The figures are mirror images of each other. Every corresponding point on the figure after a reflection is called its **image**. | • To reflect a point over the x-axis, use the same x-coordinate and multiply the y-coordinate by −1.<br>• To reflect a point over the y-axis, use the same y-coordinate and multiply the x-coordinate by −1. |
| Dilation | You enlarge or reduce a figure by a scale factor with respect to a fixed point called the center. The resulting image is similar to the original figure. | • To dilate a figure when the center of dilation is the origin, multiply each coordinate by the scale factor.<br>• To dilate a figure for any other center of dilation is not the origin, subtract the coordinates for the center of dilation from the coordinates of each point, multiply by the scale factor, and then add the coordinates for the center of dilation. |

**Example**  The vertices of figure *PQRS* are $P(-2, 2), Q(-1, 2), R(-1, -2),$ and $S(-3, -1)$. Graph the figure and its image after a reflection over the y-axis. Use the same y-coordinate and multiply the x-coordinate by −1.

| vertex | | reflection |
|---|---|---|
| $P(-2, 2)$ | → $(-2 \cdot -1, 2)$ → | $P'(2, 2)$ |
| $Q(-1, 2)$ | → $(-1 \cdot -1, 2)$ → | $Q'(1, 2)$ |
| $R(-1, -2)$ | → $(-1 \cdot -1, -2)$ → | $R'(1, -2)$ |
| $S(-3, -1)$ | → $(-3 \cdot -1, -1)$ → | $S'(3, -1)$ |

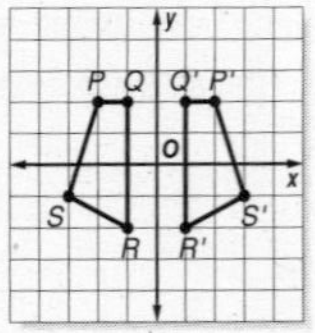

**Exercises**

For Exercises 1–3, use the graph shown.

1. Graph the image of the figure after a translation of (5, 0).

2. Graph the image of the figure after a translation of (0, 5).

3. Find the vertices of the figure after a translation of (5, 5).
$A(1, 4), B(2, 4), C(3, 3), D(4, 4), E(4, 2), \text{ and } F(1, 2)$

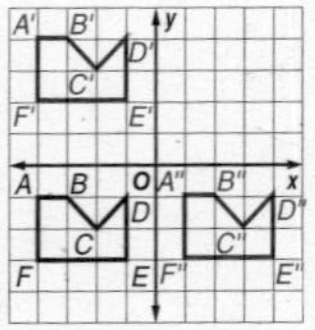

Chapter 10      18      *Glencoe Pre-Algebra*

---

# Answers (Lesson 10-3)

---

NAME _____ DATE _____ PERIOD _____

## 10-3 Word Problem Practice

### Transformations on the Coordinate Plane

1. **MAPPING** Francesca wants to rearrange her bedroom, so she drew the floor plan of her bedroom on a coordinate grid. If her bed was originally located in the second quadrant, which quadrant will it be in if she rotates its position 90° clockwise? **first quadrant**

2. **ARCHEOLOGY** Archeologists use a grid to record the location of artifacts in a dig site. An assistant marked grid A3 as the location of two arrow heads. The arrowheads were actually found in the grid 4 units to the right and 3 units down. Which grid should the assistant record as the location of the arrowheads?

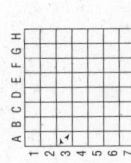

**E6**

3. **SWIMMING POOLS** Mrs. Jensen is planning to have a swimming pool installed. The contractor drew the pool on the coordinate grid. Jenny wants a bigger pool and decides a dilation with scale factor 2 centered at the origin will be sufficient. What are the coordinate of the vertices of the new pool?

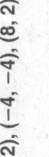

$(-4, 2), (-4, -4), (8, 2), (8, -4)$

4. **GAMES** In the game of checkers, the pieces are set up in a particular order. Which transformation would place checker A on top of checker B?

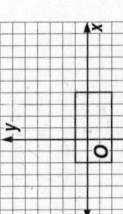

**rotation or translation**

**MODELS** For Exercises 5 and 6, use the following information.

Long-grass Landscape Company often draws a scale model of yards they are designing. The scale factor of the model shown is 1 inch to 10 feet.

5. Does this model represent a dilation, translation, or reflection of the actual yard? **dilation**

6. What will be the actual dimensions of the patio? **10 feet by 20 feet**

Chapter 10     21     Glencoe Pre-Algebra

---

NAME _____ DATE _____ PERIOD _____

## 10-3 Practice

### Transformations on the Coordinate Plane

Find the coordinates of the vertices of each figure after a reflection over the given axis. Then graph the reflection image.

1. y-axis

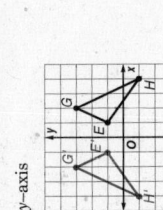

$E'(-1, 1), G'(-2, 3),$
$H'(-4, -1)$

2. x-axis

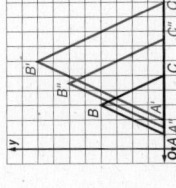

$N'(-2, 2), T'(2, 1),$
$R'(2, 3), P'(0, 4)$

3. x-axis

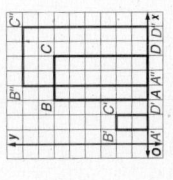

$L'(-2, 0), M'(0, 1),$
$N'(1, 0), P'(2, 4)$

**For Exercises 4–6, use the graph shown.**

4. Graph the image of the figure after a dilation centered at the origin with a scale factor of 2.

5. Graph the image of the figure after a dilation centered at the origin with a scale factor of 1.5.

6. Find the coordinates of the vertices of the figure after a dilation centered at the origin with a scale factor of $\frac{1}{2}$. $A'\left(\frac{1}{2}, 0\right), B'\left(\frac{3}{2}, 2\right)$, and $C'\left(\frac{5}{2}, 0\right)$

**For Exercises 7–9, use the graph shown.**

7. Graph the image of the figure after a dilation centered at the origin with a scale factor of $\frac{1}{3}$.

8. Find the coordinates of the vertices of the figure after a dilation centered at the origin with a scale factor of 4. $A'(12, 0), B'(12, 24), C'(24, 24),$ and $D'(24, 0)$

9. Graph the image of the figure after a dilation centered at the origin with a scale factor of $\frac{4}{3}$.

Chapter 10     20     Glencoe Pre-Algebra

# Answers (Lesson 10-3)

## 10-3 Enrichment

### Translations and Reflections

The lines on graph paper can help you draw slide images of figures.

**1.** Graph $\triangle ABC$ with vertices $A(1, 1)$, $B(-3, 4)$, and $C(-3, -4)$. Draw $\triangle A'B'C'$, the translation image of $\triangle ABC$, where the slide is 3 units to the right. Name the coordinates of the image of each vertex.

$A'(4, 1)$, $B'(0, 4)$, $C'(0, -4)$

**2.** Draw $\triangle JKL$ with vertices $J(-4, 3)$, $K(0, 2)$, and $L(-2, 0)$. Let $\triangle J'K'L'$ be the image of $\triangle JKL$ under a slide of 4 units to the right and then a slide of 3 units up. Graph $\triangle J'K'L'$. Name the coordinates of the vertices of $\triangle J'K'L'$.

$J'(0, 6)$, $K'(4, 5)$, $L'(2, 3)$

**3.** Draw $\overline{A'B'}$, the image formed by reflecting $\overline{AB}$ over the y-axis. Then draw $\overline{A''B''}$, the image formed by reflecting $\overline{A'B'}$ over the x-axis. What are the coordinates of $A''$ and $B''$? What is the relationship between the coordinates of the endpoints of $\overline{AB}$ and those of $\overline{A''B''}$?

$A''(6, -1)$, $B''(2, -5)$; The coordinates of $A''$ and $B''$ have the opposite signs of $A$ and $B$.

**4.** Draw $\overline{P'Q'}$, the reflection image of $\overline{PQ}$ over the y-axis. Draw $\overline{P'Q''}$, the reflection image of $\overline{P'Q'}$ over the x-axis. Find the slopes of $\overline{PQ}$, $\overline{P'Q'}$, and $\overline{P'Q''}$. What is the relationship between the slopes of $\overline{PQ}$ and $\overline{P'Q''}$?

Slope of $\overline{PQ} = 2$; slope of $\overline{P'Q'} = -2$; slope of $\overline{P'Q''} = 2$; They are the same.

## 10-3 Graphing Calculator Activity

### Transformations

Transformations can be graphed by using lists and scatter plots. To review lists and scatter plots, see pages 39 to 42 of your Student Edition.

**Example 1** Graph $\triangle ABC$ with $A(2, 1)$, $B(4, 3)$, and $C(6, 0)$. Then graph a triangle with a perimeter that is 3 times that of $\triangle ABC$.

Enter the $x$-coordinates of the vertices in the **L1** list. Then enter the $y$-coordinates in **L2**. Repeat the coordinates of point $A$ so that the scatter plot will form a closed figure. To graph $\triangle ABC$, turn **Plot1** on and select the connected scatter plot (⟋), and define the plot using **L1** and **L2**. Press GRAPH .

Keystrokes: STAT ENTER 2 ENTER 4 ENTER 6 ENTER 2 ENTER ▲ 1 ENTER 3 ENTER 0 ENTER 1 ENTER 2nd [STAT PLOT] ENTER ENTER ▶ ▲ ENTER 2nd [L1] ENTER ▶ [L2] ENTER GRAPH .

The vertices of a triangle with perimeter three times that of $\triangle ABC$ can be found by multiplying each coordinate of the vertices of $\triangle ABC$ by 3. Enter these vertices into **L3** and **L4**, using **L1** and **L2**.

Keystrokes: STAT ENTER ▲ 3 2nd [L1] ENTER ◀ ◀ ◀ 3 2nd [L2] ENTER .

Define **Plot2** as a connected scatter plot using **L3** and **L4**. Make sure both **Plot1** and **Plot2** are on and graph.

Keystrokes: 2nd [STAT PLOT] ▼ ENTER ENTER ▶ ENTER ▶ 2nd [L3] ENTER 2nd [L4] ENTER GRAPH .

Trace to determine the coordinates $A'(6, 3)$, $B'(12, 9)$, and $C'(18, 0)$.

**Example 2** Translate $\triangle ABC$ 2 units right and 3 units up.

Add 2 to each coordinate in **L1** and store the result in **L3**. Then add 3 to each coordinate in **L2** and store in **L4**. Then graph the plots.

Keystrokes: STAT ENTER ▲ 2nd [L1] + 2 ENTER ▲ ◀ 2nd [L2] + 3 ENTER GRAPH .

Trace to verify the new vertices $A'(10,6)$, $B'(2,4)$, and $C'(5,7)$.

**Exercises**

Find the vertices of each image for the given transformation of $\triangle ABC$ with vertices $A(-3, 1)$, $B(0, 4)$, and $C(4, -2)$.

1. dilation by a scale factor of 4  $A'(-12, 4)$, $B'(0, 16)$, and $C'(16, -8)$

2. dilation by a scale factor of $\frac{1}{2}$  $A'(-1.5, 0.5)$, $B'(0, 2)$, and $C'(2, -1)$

3. translation 6 units left and 2 units up  $A'(-9, 3)$, $B'(-6, 6)$, and $C'(-2, 0)$

4. reflection over the x-axis  $A'(-3, -1)$, $B'(0, -4)$, and $C'(4, 2)$

Chapter 10     22     Glencoe Pre-Algebra

Chapter 10     23     Glencoe Pre-Algebra

Chapter 10     **A10**     Glencoe Pre-Algebra

Copyright © Glencoe/McGraw-Hill, a division of The McGraw-Hill Companies, Inc.

# Answers (Lesson 10-4)

NAME _____ DATE _____ PERIOD _____

## 10-4 Study Guide and Intervention
### Quadrilaterals

A **quadrilateral** is a polygon with four sides and four vertices. The segments of a quadrilateral intersect only at their endpoints.

The vertices are A, B, C, and D.

The angles are ∠A, ∠B, ∠C, and ∠D.

The sides are $\overline{AB}$, $\overline{BC}$, $\overline{CD}$, and $\overline{DA}$.

A quadrilateral can be separated into two triangles. Since the sum of the measures of the angles of a triangle is 180°, the sum of the measures of the angles of a quadrilateral is 2(180°) or 360°.

**Example**  **ALGEBRA** Find the value of x. Then find each missing angle measure.

**Words**    The sum of the measures of the angles is 360°.

**Variable**  Let $m\angle A$, $m\angle B$, $m\angle C$, and $m\angle D$ represent the measures of the angles.

**Equation**  $m\angle A + m\angle B + m\angle C + m\angle D = 360$

$3x + 4x + 90 + 130 = 360$    Angles of a quadrilateral

$7x + 220 = 360$    Substitution

Combine like terms.

$7x + 220 - 220 = 360 - 220$    Subtract 220 from each side.

$7x = 140$    Simplify.

$x = 20$    Divide each side by 7.

The value of x is 20. So, $m\angle A = 3(20)$ or 60° and $m\angle B = 4(20)$ or 80°.

**Exercises**

**ALGEBRA  Find the value of x. Then find the missing angle measures.**

1. (105°, 55°, 140°, x°)   **60°; 60°**

2. (45°, 3x°, 130°, 110°)   **25°; 75°**

3. (72°, x°, 108°, 120°)   **60°; 60°**

**Classify each quadrilateral using the name that best describes it.**

4. **square**

5. **trapezoid**

6. **parallelogram**

Chapter 10   25   Glencoe Pre-Algebra

---

NAME _____ DATE _____ PERIOD _____

## 10-4 Lesson Reading Guide
### Quadrilaterals

**Get Ready for the Lesson**

**Read the introduction to Lesson 10-4 in your textbook. Write your answers below.**

a. Describe the bricks used to create the smallest circles. **squares, rectangles, trapezoids**

b. Describe how the shape of the bricks changes as the circles get larger. **Sample answer: The center of the circle is one square brick. The first row contains small trapezoids. The next four rows contain larger trapezoids. The next three rows contain trapezoids and squares that alternate.**

**Read the Lesson**

**Write a definition and give an example of the new vocabulary word.**

| Vocabulary | Definition | Example |
| --- | --- | --- |
| 1. quadrilateral | See students' work. | |

**After each description, write the correct word from the list.**

trapezoid   rhombus   parallelogram   square   rectangle

2. a parallelogram with four right angles  **rectangle**

3. a quadrilateral with both pairs of opposite sides parallel and congruent  **parallelogram**

4. a parallelogram with four congruent sides and four right angles  **square**

5. a quadrilateral with one pair of opposite sides parallel  **trapezoid**

6. a parallelogram with four congruent sides  **rhombus**

**Remember What You Learned**

7. The sum of the measures of the angles of a quadrilateral is 360°. Identify the quadrilaterals below and find the missing angle measure.

(70°, 80°, 100°, x°)   **trapezoid; 110°**

(120°, 120°, 60°, x°)   **rhombus; 60°**

(50°, 50°, 130°, x°)   **parallelogram; 130°**

Chapter 10   24   Glencoe Pre-Algebra

# Answers (Lesson 10-4)

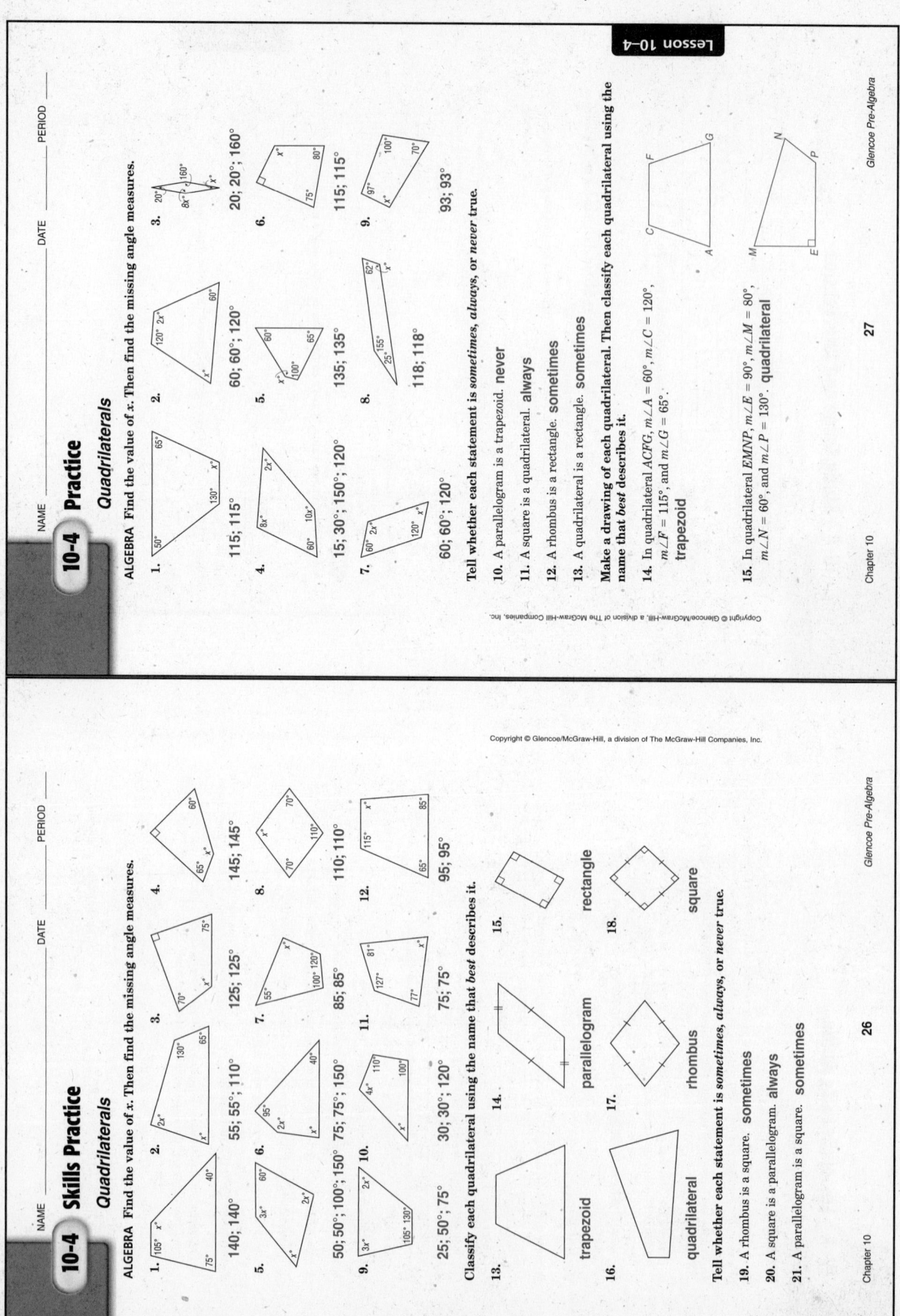

## 10-4 Practice
### Quadrilaterals

**ALGEBRA** Find the value of $x$. Then find the missing angle measures.

1. 115; 115°
2. 60; 60°; 120°
3. 20; 20°; 160°
4. 15; 30°; 150°; 120°
5. 135; 135°
6. 115°; 115°
7. 60; 60°; 120°
8. 118; 118°
9. 93; 93°

**Tell whether each statement is *sometimes*, *always*, or *never* true.**

10. A parallelogram is a trapezoid. never
11. A square is a quadrilateral. always
12. A rhombus is a rectangle. sometimes
13. A quadrilateral is a rectangle. sometimes

**Make a drawing of each quadrilateral. Then classify each quadrilateral using the name that best describes it.**

14. In quadrilateral *ACFG*, $m\angle A = 60°$, $m\angle C = 120°$, $m\angle F = 115°$, and $m\angle G = 65°$. trapezoid

15. In quadrilateral *EMNP*, $m\angle E = 90°$, $m\angle M = 80°$, $m\angle N = 60°$, and $m\angle P = 130°$. quadrilateral

## 10-4 Skills Practice
### Quadrilaterals

**ALGEBRA** Find the value of $x$. Then find the missing angle measures.

1. 140; 140°
2. 55; 55°; 110°
3. 125; 125°
4. 145; 145°
5. 50; 50°; 100°; 150°
6. 75; 75°; 150°
7. 85; 85°
8. 110; 110°
9. 25; 50°; 75°
10. 30; 30°; 120°
11. 75; 75°
12. 95; 95°

**Classify each quadrilateral using the name that best describes it.**

13. trapezoid
14. parallelogram
15. rectangle
16. quadrilateral
17. rhombus
18. square

**Tell whether each statement is *sometimes*, *always*, or *never* true.**

19. A rhombus is a square. sometimes
20. A square is a parallelogram. always
21. A parallelogram is a square. sometimes

# Answers (Lesson 10-4)

## 10-4 Enrichment

### Using Coordinates

**For Exercises 1–4, use the coordinate grid at the right.**

1. Graph the points (1, 1), (4, 4), and (2, 4). Connect the dots. Name the figure formed.   **triangle**

2. Multiply each y-coordinate in Exercise 1 by −1. Graph the points. How is this triangle related to the one in Exercise 1?   **It is a reflection over the x-axis.**

3. Multiply each coordinate in Exercise 1 by −1. Graph the points.

4. What would you have to do to get the coordinates of a triangle in Quadrant II congruent to the ones in Exercises 1–3?   **Multiply each x-coordinate in Exercise 1 by −1.**

**For Exercises 5–10, use the coordinate grid at the right.**

5. Graph the points (3, 1), (2, 3), (4, 6), and (5, 4). Connect the dots. The figure formed is called a parallelogram.

6. Add 2 to both coordinates of each point and graph the new coordinates. Name the figure formed.   **parallelogram**

7. Add −4 to the x-coordinate of each point in Exercise 5 and graph the new coordinates. Is this figure also a parallelogram?   **yes**

8. Graph the points (5, −2), (6, −3), (5, −5), and (3, −3) on the coordinate plane at the right. Name the figure formed.   **trapezoid**

9. Multiply both coordinates of each point in Exercise 8 by 2 and graph the new coordinates. This is an enlargement.

10. Multiply both coordinates of each point in Exercise 8 by $\frac{1}{2}$ and graph the new coordinates. This is a reduction.

---

## 10-4 Word Problem Practice

### Quadrilaterals

1. **KITES** Yashika got a new kite for her birthday. What quadrilateral best describes the shape of this kite?

**rhombus**

2. **PLANTERS** A city used large tree planters to line the road. Identify as many different quadrilaterals as possible in the planters.

**square, trapezoid**

3. **PROPERTY** Mr. Orwell has some property in the middle of the wilderness. The shape of the property is a quadrilateral. Mr. Orwell knows the angles of intersections of three sides are 28°, 147°, and 72°. What is the measure of the fourth angle of the property?   **113°**

4. **WINDOWS** The window above the front door in Heather's home is shown below. Find the measures of angles 1, 2, and 3.

$m\angle 1 = 70°$, $m\angle 2 = 70°$, $m\angle 3 = 110°$

**DESIGN For Exercises 5–7, use the following information.**

Diego is going to design a kite. Two of the opposite angles are congruent. One of the other angles is half the congruent angles, and the other is twice the congruent angles.

5. Make a sketch of the kite.

6. Write an equation to find the measures of the four angles of the kite.   $2x + x + x + \frac{1}{2}x = 360$

7. What are the measures of the four angles?   **40°, 80°, 80°, 160°**

---

NAME _____ DATE _____ PERIOD _____

## 10-5 Study Guide and Intervention

### Polygons

A **polygon** is a simple, closed figure formed by three or more coplanar line segments. The line segments, called *sides*, meet only at their endpoints. The points of intersection are called *vertices*. Polygons can be classified by the number of sides they have.

A **diagonal** is a line segment in a polygon that joins two nonconsecutive vertices, forming triangles. You can use the property of the sum of the measures of the angles of a triangle to find the sum of the measures of the interior angles of any polygon.
An **interior angle** is an angle inside a polygon.

| Number of Sides | Name of Polygon |
|---|---|
| 3 | triangle |
| 4 | quadrilateral |
| 5 | pentagon |
| 6 | hexagon |
| 7 | heptagon |
| 8 | octagon |
| 9 | nonagon |
| 10 | decagon |

If a polygon has *n* sides, then *n* − 2 triangles are formed. The sum of the degree measures of the interior angles of the polygon is (*n* − 2)180.

A regular polygon is a polygon that is *equilateral* (all sides are congruent) and *equiangular* (all angles are congruent). Since the angles of a regular polygon are congruent, their measures are equal.

**Example** **Find the measure of one interior angle of a regular 20-gon.**

**Step 1** A 20-gon has 20 sides. Therefore, *n* = 20.

(*n* − 2)180 = (20 − 2)180    Replace *n* with 20.

= 18(180) or 3240    Simplify.

The sum of the measures of the interior angles is 3240°.

**Step 2** Divide the sum by 20 to find the measure of one angle.

3240 ÷ 20 = 162

So, the measure of one interior angle in a regular 20-gon is 162°.

**Exercises**

**Classify each polygon. Then determine whether it appears to be *regular* or *not regular*.**

1.

heptagon; not regular

2.

octagon; not regular

3.

quadrilateral; regular

**Find the sum of the measures of the interior angles of each polygon.**

4. quadrilateral    5. nonagon    6. heptagon    7. 12-gon
   360°               1260°          900°            1800°

---

NAME _____ DATE _____ PERIOD _____

## 10-5 Lesson Reading Guide

### Polygons

**Get Ready for the Lesson**

**Read the introduction to Lesson 10-5 in your textbook. Write your answers below.**

a. Which figure is used to create each tessellation?
   **square, triangle, hexagon**

b. Refer to the diagram in your textbook. What is the sum of the measures of the angles that surround the vertex? **360°**

c. Does the sum in part **b** hold true for the square tessellation? Explain. **Yes; for each tessellation shown, the sum of the measures of the angles that surround a vertex is 360°.**

d. Make a conjecture about the sum of the measures of the angles that surround a vertex in the hexagon tessellation. **The sum is 360°.**

**Read the Lesson** **1–3. See students' work.**

**Write a definition and give an example of each new vocabulary word or phrase.**

| Vocabulary | Definition | Example |
|---|---|---|
| 1. diagonal | | |
| 2. interior angles | | |
| 3. regular polygon | | |

**Remember What You Learned**

4. Complete the following concept map of how to find the sum of the measures of the interior angles of a regular polygon (all sides and angles are congruent) and how to find the measure of one interior angle.

**Step 1** Count the polygon's sides or vertices.

**Step 2** Subtract 2 from this number and multiply by 180 to find sum of the measures of the interior angles.

**Step 3** Divide this sum by the number of sides/vertices to find the measure of one interior angle.

## 10-5 Practice

*Polygons*

**Find the sum of the measures of the interior angles of each polygon.**

1. quadrilateral  360°
2. decagon  1440°
3. 12-gon  1800°
4. heptagon  900°
5. pentagon  540°
6. hexagon  720°
7. 25-gon  4140°
8. 100-gon  17,640°

**Find the measure of an interior angle of each polygon.**

9. regular nonagon  140°
10. regular octagon  135°
11. regular hexagon  120°
12. regular 12-gon  150°
13. regular quadrilateral  90°
14. regular decagon  144°

**TESSELLATIONS** For Exercises 15 and 16, identify the polygons used to create each tessellation.

15. triangles, quadrilaterals, hexagons, octagons

16. triangles, squares, hexagons, octagons

17. Which figure best represents a regular polygon?  D

A B C D

---

## 10-5 Skills Practice

*Polygons*

**Classify each polygon. Then determine whether it appears to be *regular* or *not regular*.**

1. hexagon; not regular
2. octagon; regular
3. quadrilateral; regular
4. 12-gon; regular
5. pentagon; not regular
6. heptagon; not regular

**Find the sum of the measures of the interior angles of each polygon.**

7. pentagon  540°
8. 20-gon  3240°
9. nonagon  1260°
10. decagon  1440°

**Find the measure of an interior angle of each polygon.**

11. regular hexagon  120°
12. regular heptagon  128.6°
13. regular quadrilateral  90°
14. regular octagon  135°
15. regular pentagon  108°
16. regular 100-gon  176.4°

**TESSELLATIONS** For Exercises 17 and 18, identify the polygons used to create each tessellation.

17. hexagon, pentagons, triangles

18. pentagons, squares, triangles, decagon

# Answers (Lesson 10-5)

---

## 10-5 Word Problem Practice

### Polygons

NAME _____ DATE _____ PERIOD _____

1. **TRAFFIC SIGNS** A familiar sight to many people is the red STOP sign found at street corners and intersections. The shape of the STOP sign is shown below. Classify the polygon and determine if it appears to be regular or not regular.

**STOP**

**octagon; regular**

2. **NUTS AND BOLTS** The nut to a standard bolt is a regular hexagon. What is the sum of the measures of the interior angles of the nut?

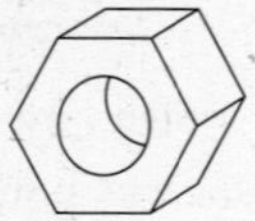

**720°**

3. **WINDOWS** Some older houses have regular octagonal windows. What would be the measure of one of the interior angles in this type of window? **135°**

4. **AREA RUGS** The pattern in an area rug is shown below. Identify the three different polygons used to create the pattern.

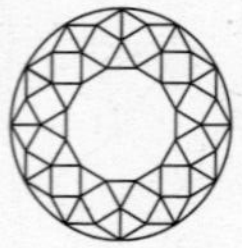

**quadrilateral; triangle; dodecagon**

**SYMBOLS** For Exercises 5–7, use the following information.

Jenna made this shape with patterns blocks.

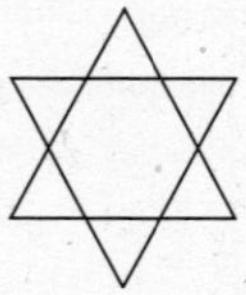

5. This design can be made up of 7 regular polygons. What are they? **6 regular triangles and 1 regular hexagon**

6. This design is also made of one dodecagon. What is the sum of the measures of all the interior angles of the dodecagon? **1800°**

7. What are the measures of the interior angles of the dodecagon? **6 angles of 60°, 6 angles of 240°**

---

## 10-5 Enrichment

NAME _____ DATE _____ PERIOD _____

### Polygons and Diagonals

A **diagonal** of a polygon is any segment that connects two nonconsecutive vertices of the polygon. In each of the following polygons, all possible diagonals are drawn.

**Example**

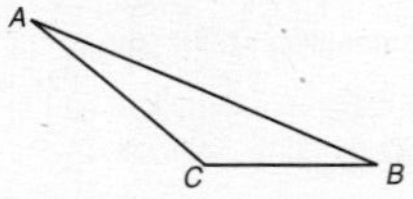

In $\triangle ABC$, no diagonals can be drawn. Why?

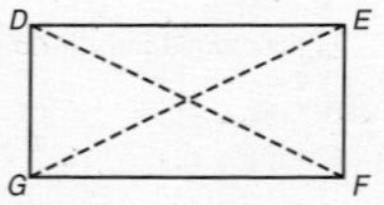

In quadrilateral *DEFG*, 2 diagonals can be drawn.

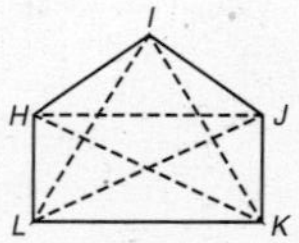

In pentagon *HIJKL*, 5 diagonals can be drawn.

Complete the chart below and try to find a pattern that will help you answer the questions that follow.

| Polygons | Number of Sides | Number of Diagonals from One Vertex | Total Number of Diagonals |
|---|---|---|---|
| triangle | 3 | 0 | 0 |
| quadrilateral | 4 | 1 | 2 |
| pentagon | 5 | 2 | 5 |
| 1. hexagon | 6 | **3** | **9** |
| 2. heptagon | 7 | **4** | **14** |
| 3. octagon | 8 | **5** | **20** |
| 4. nonagon | 9 | **6** | **27** |
| 5. decagon | 10 | **7** | **35** |

Find the total number of diagonals that can be drawn in a polygon with the given number of sides.

6. 6 **9**     7. 7 **14**    8. 8 **20**    9. 9 **27**

10. 10 **35**    11. 11 **44**    12. 12 **54**    13. 15 **90**

14. 20 **170**    15. 50 **1175**    16. 75 **2700**

17. $n$   $\dfrac{n^2 - 3n}{2}$

# Answers (Lesson 10-6)

NAME _____ DATE _____ PERIOD _____

## 10-6 Study Guide and Intervention

### Area: Parallelograms, Triangles, and Trapezoids

| Shape | Words | Area Formula | Model |
|---|---|---|---|
| Parallelogram | The area of a parallelogram can be found by multiplying the measures of the base and the height. | $A = bh$ | 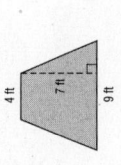 |
| Triangle | A diagonal of a parallelogram separates the parallelogram into two congruent triangles. The area of each triangle is one-half the area of the parallelogram. | $A = \frac{1}{2}bh$ | |
| Trapezoid | A trapezoid has two bases. The height of a trapezoid is the distance between the bases. A trapezoid can be separated into two triangles. | $A = \frac{1}{2}h(a + b)$ | |

**Example** Find the area of the trapezoid.

$A = \frac{1}{2}h(a + b)$    Area of a trapezoid

$A = \frac{1}{2} \cdot 17(7 + 26)$    Replace $h$ with 17, $a$ with 7, and $b$ with 26.

$A = \frac{1}{2} \cdot 17 \cdot 33$    $7 + 26 = 33$

$A = \frac{561}{2}$ or $280\frac{1}{2}$

The area of the trapezoid is $280\frac{1}{2}$ mm².

**Exercises**

Find the area of each figure.

1.

**3 cm²**

2.

**7.5 m²**

3.

**97.5 ft²**

Find the area of each figure described.

4. trapezoid: height, 12 yd; bases, 6 yd, 8 yd    **84 yd²**

5. parallelogram: base, 4.5 cm; height, 8 cm    **36 cm²**

Chapter 10    37    *Glencoe Pre-Algebra*

---

NAME _____ DATE _____ PERIOD _____

## 10-6 Lesson Reading Guide

### Area: Parallelograms, Triangles, and Trapezoids

**Get Ready for the Lesson**

Read the introduction to Lesson 10-6 in your textbook. Write your answers below.

a. Compare the area of the rectangle to the area of the parallelogram. **They are the same.**

b. What parts of a rectangle and parallelogram determine their area? **height and base**

**Read the Lesson** 1–2. **See students' work.**

Write a definition and give an example of each new vocabulary word.

| Vocabulary | Definition | Example |
|---|---|---|
| 1. base | | |
| 2. altitude | | |

**Remember What You Learned**

3. Below are three figures and three formulas for finding area. Match the formula with the correct figure and find its area.

$A = \frac{1}{2}h(a + b)$     $A = bh$     $A = \frac{1}{2}bh$

Formula: $A = \frac{1}{2}bh$    Formula: $A = bh$    Formula: $A = \frac{1}{2}h(a + b)$

Area: **52.5 cm²**    Area: **48 in²**    Area: **45.5 ft²**

Chapter 10    36    *Glencoe Pre-Algebra*

# Answers (Lesson 10-6)

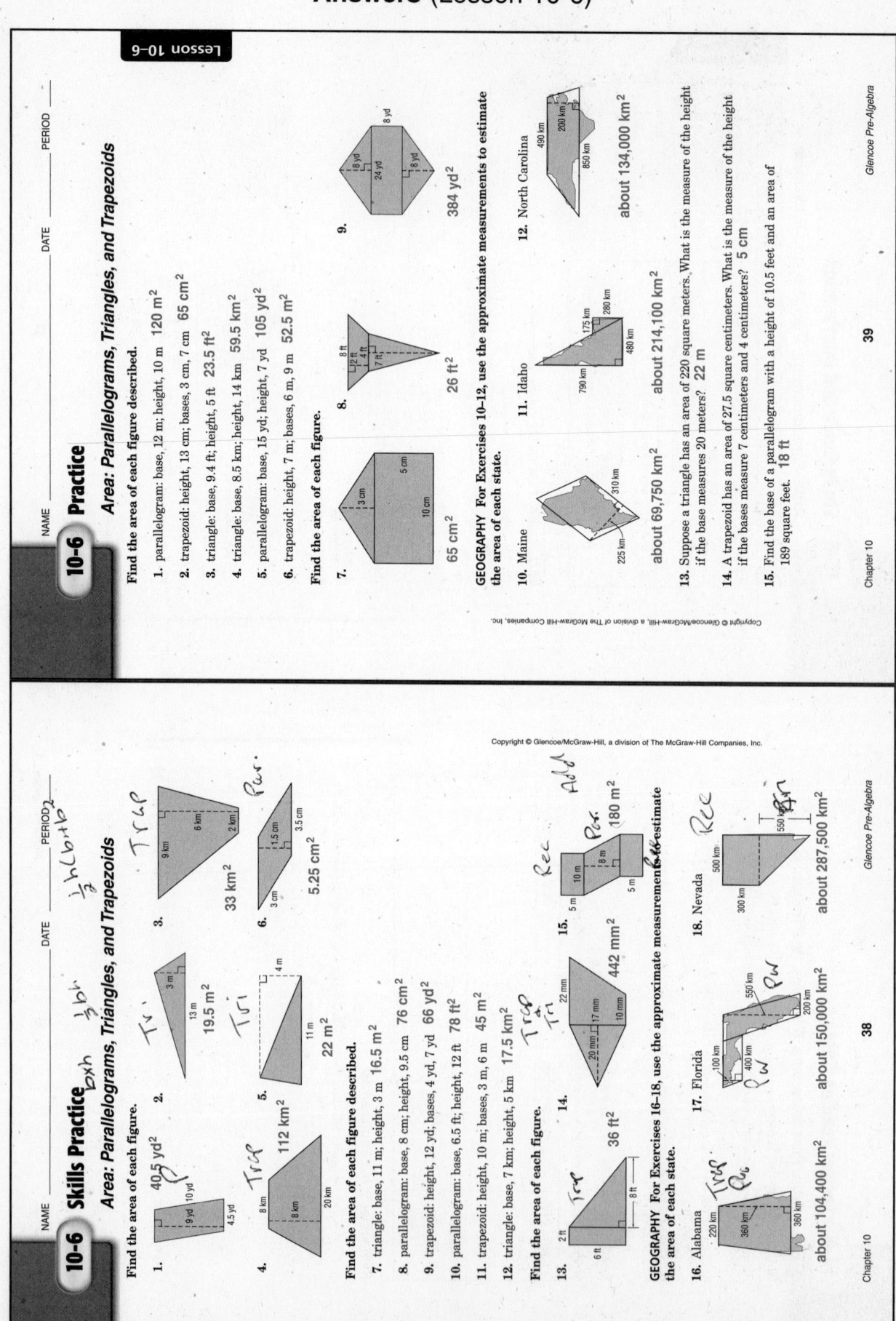

## Lesson 10-6

NAME _____ DATE _____ PERIOD _____

### 10-6 Practice

**Area: Parallelograms, Triangles, and Trapezoids**

**Find the area of each figure described.**

1. parallelogram: base, 12 m; height, 10 m   120 m²

2. trapezoid: height, 13 cm; bases, 3 cm, 7 cm   65 cm²

3. triangle: base, 9.4 ft; height, 5 ft   23.5 ft²

4. triangle: base, 8.5 km; height, 14 km   59.5 km²

5. parallelogram: base, 15 yd; height, 7 yd   105 yd²

6. trapezoid: height, 7 m; bases, 6 m, 9 m   52.5 m²

**Find the area of each figure.**

7.
65 cm²

8.
26 ft²

9.
384 yd²

**GEOGRAPHY For Exercises 10–12, use the approximate measurements to estimate the area of each state.**

10. Maine
about 69,750 km²

11. Idaho
about 214,100 km²

12. North Carolina
about 134,000 km²

13. Suppose a triangle has an area of 220 square meters. What is the measure of the height if the base measures 20 meters?   22 m

14. A trapezoid has an area of 27.5 square centimeters. What is the measure of the height if the bases measure 7 centimeters and 4 centimeters?   5 cm

15. Find the base of a parallelogram with a height of 10.5 feet and an area of 189 square feet.   18 ft

Chapter 10    39    Glencoe Pre-Algebra

---

NAME _____ DATE _____ PERIOD _____

### 10-6 Skills Practice

**Area: Parallelograms, Triangles, and Trapezoids**

**Find the area of each figure.**

1.
40.5 yd²

2.
19.5 m²

3.
33 km²

4.
112 km²

5.
22 m²

6.
5.25 cm²

**Find the area of each figure described.**

7. triangle: base, 11 m; height, 3 m   16.5 m²

8. parallelogram: base, 8 cm; height, 9.5 cm   76 cm²

9. trapezoid: height, 12 yd; bases, 4 yd, 7 yd   66 yd²

10. parallelogram: base, 6.5 ft; height, 12 ft   78 ft²

11. trapezoid: height, 10 m; bases, 3 m, 6 m   45 m²

12. triangle: base, 7 km; height, 5 km   17.5 km²

**Find the area of each figure.**

13.
36 ft²

14.
442 mm²

15.
180 m²

**GEOGRAPHY For Exercises 16–18, use the approximate measurements to estimate the area of each state.**

16. Alabama
about 104,400 km²

17. Florida
about 150,000 km²

18. Nevada
about 287,500 km²

Chapter 10    38    Glencoe Pre-Algebra

# Answers (Lesson 10-6)

## 10-6 Word Problem Practice

### Area: Parallelograms, Triangles, and Trapezoids

**1. FLOOR PLANS** Matt's bedroom is shaped like a parallelogram. His parents have decided to buy a new carpet for his room. If two opposite walls are 12 feet long and the distance between these walls is 8 feet, how many square feet of carpet will they need to buy?

**96 square feet**

**2. SAILBOATS** A sailboat has a triangular sail with a height of 18 feet and the base of 12 feet. What is the area of the sail?

**108 square feet**

**3. TILING** Mrs. Sanchez wants to tile her bathroom floor. The floor is 5 feet wide and 8 feet long. The tiles Mrs. Sanchez wants to use are 4 inch squares. How many tiles will she need to cover the bathroom floor? **360 tiles**

**4. GLASS COSTS** Mrs. Humphrey needs to replace a broken window at her house. The window is shaped like a trapezoid with the dimensions shown below. If glass costs $4.50 per square foot, how much will the replacement window cost?

21 in.
18 in.
42 in.

**$17.72**

**SYMBOLS** For Exercises 5–7, use the following information.

Melanie wants to cut her cake into triangular wedges to serve at her party. She cannot decide what kind of triangle to cut. She tries two possible triangular wedges.

6 in.
4 in.
8 in.
3 in.
Piece 1
Piece 2

**5.** What is the area of the first wedge? What is the area of the second wedge? Both pieces are 12 square inches.

**6.** Sketch and label another triangular wedge with the same area. **Sample answer:**

4 in.
6 in.

**7.** Melanie wants each guest to have the same amount of cake. If there are 54 guests at the party, what should the dimensions of the cake be so that everyone gets the same amount of cake?
**36 inches by 18 inches**

---

## 10-6 Enrichment

### Area of an Equilateral Triangle

The area of an equilateral triangle is the product of one fourth of the square of a side times the square root of 3 (which is approximately 1.732).

$$A = \frac{1}{4} s^2 (\sqrt{3})$$

or $A \approx \frac{s^2}{4} (1.732)$

**Example**

10 cm

$$A \approx \frac{10^2}{4} (1.732)$$
$$\approx \frac{100}{4} (1.732)$$
$$\approx 43.3$$

The area of the triangle is approximately 43.3 cm².

**Find the area of each equilateral triangle. Round each answer to the nearest tenth.**

**1.** 5 m
**10.8 m²**

**2.** 15 mm
**97.4 mm²**

**3.** 8 in.
**27.7 in²**

**4.** 3 yd
**3.9 yd²**

**5.** 5.1 cm
**11.3 cm²**

**6.** 4.3 m
**8.0 m²**

**7.** $2\frac{1}{2}$ ft
**2.7 ft²**

**8.** $3\frac{1}{3}$ yd
**4.8 yd²**

**9.** 9.3 cm
**37.5 cm²**

**10.** 0.8 m
**0.3 m²**

**11.** $5\frac{2}{3}$ ft
**13.9 ft²**

**12.** 0.74 m
**0.2 m²**

---

## Lesson 10-7

## 10-7 Lesson Reading Guide

### Circles: Circumference and Area

**Get Ready for the Lesson**

Read the introduction to Lesson 10-7 in your textbook. Write your answers below.

a. Collect three different-sized circular objects. Then copy the table shown. **See students' work.**

b. Using a tape measure, measure each distance below to the nearest millimeter. Record your results.

  • the distance across the circular object through its center (*d*)

  • the distance around each circular object (*C*) **See students' work.**

c. For each object, find the ratio $\frac{C}{d}$. Record the results in the table. **The results are about 3.**

d. Write an equation that relates circumference *C* of a circle to its diameter *d*. $C \approx 3d$

**Read the Lesson** 1–6. **See students' work.**

Write a definition and give an example of each new vocabulary word.

| Vocabulary | Definition | Example |
|---|---|---|
| 1. circle | | |
| 2. diameter | | |
| 3. center | | |
| 4. circumference | | |
| 5. radius | | |
| 6. π (pi) | | |

**Remember What You Learned**

7. Study the circle at the right, label each part, then find the circle's circumference and area (round to the nearest tenth).

formula for circumference: $C = \pi d$ or $2\pi r$

formula for area: $A = \pi r^2$

circumference: **15.7 cm**

area: **19.6 cm²**

---

## Lesson 10-6

## 10-6 Spreadsheet Activity

### Maximum Area of a Parallelogram

You can use cardboard strips, paper fasteners, and a spreadsheet to investigate how changing the height of a parallelogram with a fixed perimeter changes the area of the parallelogram.

**Step 1** Cut two pairs of cardboard strips. Construct a parallelogram by fastening the strips together at the corners as shown at the right. Label the vertices *A*, *B*, *C*, and *D*.

**Step 2** Move the sides of the parallelogram so that the measure of angle *A* is small. Use a centimeter ruler to measure the base and the height of the parallelogram. Enter the data in Columns A and B of the spreadsheet. Use Column C for the formula for the area of the parallelogram.

**Step 3** Move the sides of the parallelogram to increase the measure of angle *A* and measure the base and the height again. Record the data. Continue changing the parallelogram, measuring and recording data until you have at least 6 different pairs of measures.

| | A | B | C |
|---|---|---|---|
| 1 | Base | Height | Area |
| 2 | | | =A2*B2 |
| 3 | | | =A3*B3 |
| 4 | | | =A4*B4 |

Sheet 1 / Sheet 2

**Exercises**

**Refer to the spreadsheet.**

1. What happens to the measure of the base as you increase the measure of angle *A*? **The measure of the base remains the same.**

2. What happens to the measure of the height as you increase the measure of angle *A*? **The measure of the height increases as you increase the measure of angle *A*.**

3. How is the area of the parallelogram affected as you increase the measure of angle *A*? **The area increases as you increase the measure of angle *A*.**

4. Notice that since the sides of parallelogram *ABCD* are fixed, the perimeter is unchanged as the measure of angle *A* is changed. Make a conjecture about the measure of angle *A* when the area of *ABCD* is the greatest. Use a protractor to verify your conjecture. **The measure of angle *A* is 90° and *ABCD* is a rectangle when the area of the parallelogram is greatest.**

---

## Left Page — Study Guide and Intervention

NAME _____ DATE _____ PERIOD _____

# 10-7 Study Guide and Intervention

## Circles: Circumference and Area

**Circles**

A **circle** is the set of all points in a plane that are the same distance from a given point.

The circumference of a circle is equal to its diameter times $\pi$, or 2 times its radius times $\pi$.  $C = \pi d$ or $C = 2\pi r$

The area of a circle is equal to $\pi$ times the square or its radius.  $A = \pi r^2$

**Example 1**

Find the circumference of the circle to the nearest tenth.

a.

$C = 2\pi r$    Circumference of a circle
$C = 2 \cdot \pi \cdot 7$    Replace $r$ with 7.
$C \approx 44.0$    Simplify. Use a calculator.

The circumference is about 44.0 kilometers.

**Example 2**

Find the area of the circle. Round to the nearest tenth.

b.

$A = \pi r^2$    Area of a circle
$A = \pi \cdot (15)^2$    Replace $r$ with 15.
$A = \pi \cdot 225$    Evaluate $(15)^2$.
$A \approx 706.9$    Use a calculator.

The area is about 706.9 square inches.

**Exercises**

Find the circumference and area of each circle. Round to the nearest tenth.

1. 31.4 m; 78.5 m²
2. 22.0 m; 38.5 m²
3. 50.3 cm; 201.1 cm²
4. 37.7 ft; 113.1 ft²

Match each circle described in the column on the left with corresponding measurement in the column on the right.

5. radius: 5 units   c
6. diameter: 9 units   a
7. diameter: 12 units   d
8. diameter: 16 units   b

a. area: 63.6 units²
b. circumference: 50.3 units
c. circumference: 31.4 units
d. area: 113.1 units²

## Right Page — Skills Practice

NAME _____ DATE _____ PERIOD _____

# 10-7 Skills Practice

## Circles: Circumference and Area

Find the circumference and area of each circle. Round to the nearest tenth.

1. 56.5 m; 254.5 m²
2. 53.4 ft; 227.0 ft²
3. 9.4 yd; 7.1 yd²
4. 15.7 cm; 19.6 cm²

5. The radius is 7 kilometers. 44.0 km; 153.9 km²
6. The diameter is 20 centimeters. 62.8 cm; 314.2 cm²
7. The diameter is 8.5 meters. 26.7 m; 56.7 m²
8. The radius is 11 yards. 69.1 yd; 380.1 yd²
9. The diameter is $6\frac{2}{5}$ feet. 20.1 ft; 32.2 ft²
10. The radius is 25 inches. 157.1 in.; 1963.5 in²

Match each circle described in the column on the left with its corresponding measurement in the column on the right.

11. diameter: 6 units   c
12. radius: 9 units   d
13. diameter: 13 units   b
14. radius: 2.5 units   a

a. area: 19.6 units²
b. circumference: 40.8 units
c. area: 28.3 units²
d. circumference: 56.5 units

15. **SPORTS** A basketball goal is 18 inches in diameter. A basketball has a diameter of about 9.6 inches. What is the difference in area between the goal and the center cross-section of a basketball? **182.1 in²**

16. **CULTURE** The Navajo and Pueblo Indians create large, circular sand paintings as part of traditional healing ceremonies. How much more area does a sand painting with a 20-foot diameter have compared with one with a 5-foot diameter? **294.5 ft²**

17. **SPORT** In bowling, the distance from the foul line to the headpin is 60 feet. A bowling ball has a radius of about 4.3 inches. How many times must the ball rotate in order to strike the headpin? 26.6 ≈ 27 times

Find the area of each figure. Round to the nearest tenth.

18. 271.0 in²
19. 114.3 cm²

# Answers (Lesson 10-7)

NAME _____ DATE _____ PERIOD _____

## 10-7 Practice

### Circles: Circumference and Area

**Find the circumference and area of each circle. Round to the nearest tenth.**

1. The diameter is 18 yards.
   56.5 yd; 254.5 yd²

2. The radius is 4 meters.
   25.1 m; 50.3 m²

3. The diameter is 4.2 meters.
   13.2 m; 13.9 m²

4. The radius is 4.5 feet.
   28.3 ft; 63.6 ft²

5. The radius is $9\frac{3}{4}$ miles.
   61.3 mi; 298.6 mi²

6. The diameter is 6 kilometers.
   18.8 km; 28.3 km²

**Match each circle described in the column on the left with its corresponding measurement in the column on the right.**

7. radius: 8.5 units **a**

8. diameter: 9 units **c**

9. diameter: 6.5 units **b**

10. radius: 12 units **d**

a. circumference: 53.4 units

b. area: 33.2 units²

c. area: 63.6 units²

d. circumference: 75.4 units

11. **SPORTS** A baseball has a radius of about 1.5 inches. Home plate is 16 inches wide. If a baseball were rolled across home plate, how many complete rotations would it take to cover the distance? **2 complete rotations**

12. **SPORTS** A soccer ball has a circumference of about 28 inches, while the goal is 24 feet wide. How many soccer balls would be needed to cover the distance between the goalposts? **33 soccer balls**

13. **HISTORY** Chariot races reached their peak in popularity in ancient Rome around the 1st and 2nd centuries A.D. A chariot wheel had a radius of about one foot. One lap around the track in the Circus Maximus was approximately 2,300 feet. How many chariot-wheel revolutions did it take to complete one lap? **about 366 revolutions**

14. **CULTURE** One of the artistic traditions of Tantric Buddhism is *dul–tson–kyil–khor*, which is the creation of intricately designed prayer circles (called mandalas) using colored sand. The sand is funneled through a hollow metal tube about 0.5 centimeter in diameter. If the prayer circle were a meter across, approximately how many funnel-tips of sand would be needed to cover its surface? **40,000 funnel-tips**

---

NAME _____ DATE _____ PERIOD _____

## 10-7 Word Problem Practice

### Circles: Circumference and Area

1. **TREES** A tree on Joanne's property has a circumference of 6.8 feet. What is the diameter of the tree? **2.16 feet**

2. **DOGS** Carl's dog, Buddy, is on an 8-foot leash that is attached to the center of a 20-foot fence. How much space does Buddy have to roam around?

   **100.53 square feet**

3. **KITCHEN FURNITURE** Mr. Margulies bought four new stools for his kitchen. Each stool top has a diameter of 14 inches. Mr. Margulies wants to make pads for each stool. The padding is three cents per square inch. How much will Mr. Margulies spend in padding for the four stools? **$18.47**

4. **TOYS** Josh has a large plastic disc that he uses to play catch with his dog. The disc has a radius of 6 inches. What is the area of the disc? **113.1 square inches**

**PIZZA For Exercises 5–7, use the following information.**

At Paco's Pizza Shop, a large pizza has a diameter of 16 inches. A small pizza has a diameter of 12 inches.

5. What is the area of the small pizza? What is the area of the large pizza? **large: 201.06 in² small: 113.10 in²**

6. A large pizza costs $9.95 and a small pizza costs $5.95. Which pizza is a better deal? Explain. **A large pizza is the better deal. The price per square inch for the large pizza is less than the price per square inch for the small pizza.**

7. On Tuesday's, Paco's Pizza has a special, two small pizzas for $11.25. Is this truly a special price? Explain your reasoning. **No, a large pizza is still cheaper per square inch.**

# Answers (Lessons 10-7 and 10-8)

## 10-8 Lesson Reading Guide

### Area: Composite Figures

**Get Ready for the Lesson**

Read the introduction to Lesson 10-8 in your textbook. Write your answers below.

In the diagram, the area of California is separated into polygons.

a. Identify the polygons. **two trapezoids, a triangle, and a rectangle**

b. Explain how polygons can be used to estimate the total land area. **Add the areas to find the total area.**

c. What is the area of each region? **large trapezoid: 79,800 sq mi; triangle: 41,062 sq mi; small trapezoid: 16,000 sq mi; rectangle: 21,328 sq mi**

d. What is the total area? **158,190 sq mi**

**Read the Lesson**

Complete the following statements by filling in the blanks with the following words or symbols.

| triangle | $A = \frac{1}{2}h(a+b)$ | separating | formula | $A = bh$ |
|---|---|---|---|---|
| trapezoid | $A = \pi r^2$ | area | composite figure | |

1. The area of a(n) **composite figure** can be determined by **separating** the figure into simple polygons.

2. Each separate polygon has a specific **formula** to determine its area. For a circle, it's $A = \pi r^2$, while $A = \frac{1}{2}bh$ works for a **triangle**.

3. To find the area of a parallelogram, the formula **$A = bh$** should be applied.

4. A(n) **trapezoid**, on the other hand, requires the formula $A = \frac{1}{2}h(a+b)$.

5. To find the **area** of the whole figure, the areas of the polygons are added together.

**Remember What You Learned**

6. Study the figure below, identify the separate polygons, find the area of each polygon, and find the area of the entire figure. Round to the nearest tenth.

area of polygon 1: **9.8 in²**

area of polygon 2: **15 in²**

area of polygon 3: **80 in²**

total area of figure: **104.8 in²**

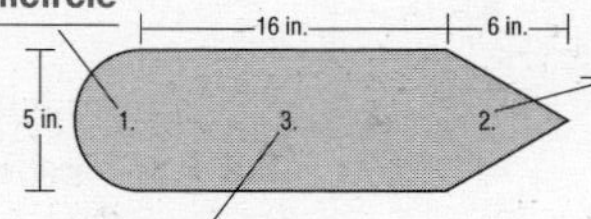

49

Chapter 10                                   Glencoe Pre-Algebra

---

## 10-7 Enrichment

### Sector of a Circle

The sector of a circle is the region bounded by two radii and the arc of the circle. The area of a sector is a fractional part of the area of the circle.

$A = \frac{n}{360} \times \pi \times r^2$ where $n$ is the degree measure of the central angle.

**Example**

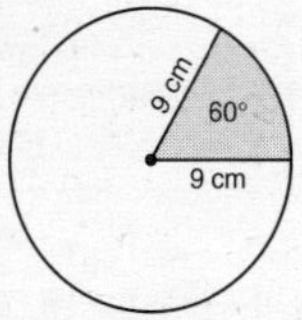

Area of a sector $\approx \frac{60}{360} \times 3.14 \times 81$

$\approx 42.39$ cm²

**Find the area of each sector. Use 3.14 for $\pi$.**

1. **56.52 cm²**

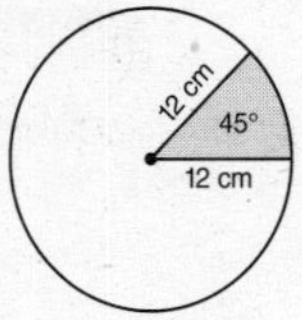

2. **37.68 cm²**

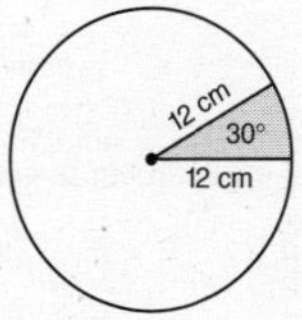

3. **75.36 cm²**

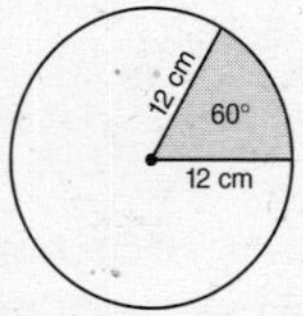

4. **28.26 cm²**

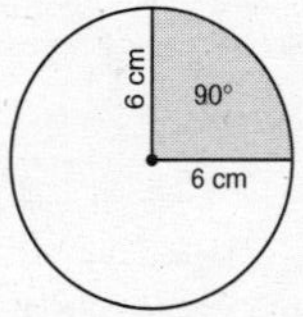

5. **18.84 cm²**

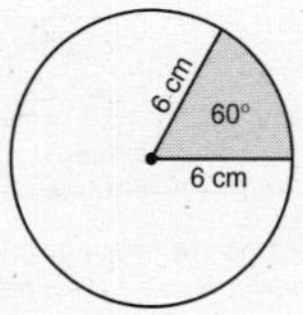

6. **84.78 cm²**

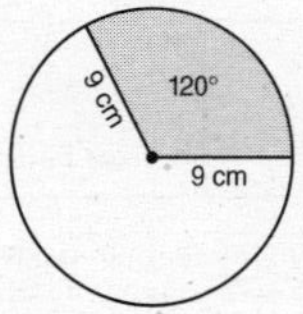

48

Chapter 10                                   Glencoe Pre-Algebra

---

# Answers (Lesson 10-8)

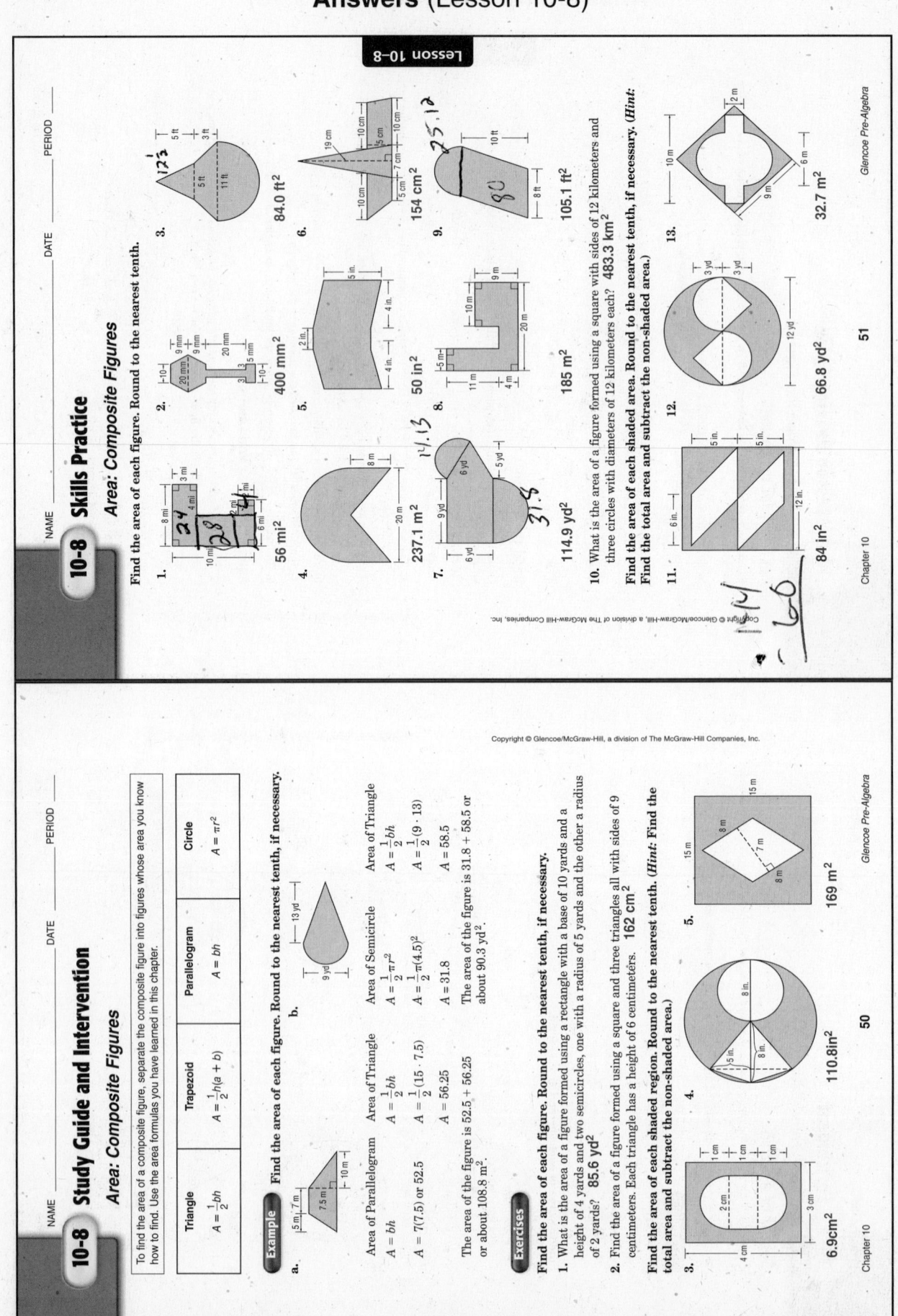

NAME _____ DATE _____ PERIOD _____

## 10-8 Skills Practice

### Area: Composite Figures

**Find the area of each figure. Round to the nearest tenth.**

1. 56 mi²

2. 400 mm²

3. 84.0 ft²

4. 237.1 m²

5. 50 in²

6. 154 cm²

7. 114.9 yd²

8. 185 m²

9. 105.1 ft²

10. What is the area of a figure formed using a square with sides of 12 kilometers and three circles with diameters of 12 kilometers each? 483.3 km²

**Find the area of each shaded area. Round to the nearest tenth, if necessary. (Hint: Find the total area and subtract the non-shaded area.)**

11. 84 in²

12. 66.8 yd²

13. 32.7 m²

Chapter 10    51    Glencoe Pre-Algebra

---

NAME _____ DATE _____ PERIOD _____

## 10-8 Study Guide and Intervention

### Area: Composite Figures

To find the area of a composite figure, separate the composite figure into figures whose area you know how to find. Use the area formulas you have learned in this chapter.

| Triangle | Trapezoid | Parallelogram | Circle |
|---|---|---|---|
| $A = \frac{1}{2}bh$ | $A = \frac{1}{2}h(a + b)$ | $A = bh$ | $A = \pi r^2$ |

**Example**   **Find the area of each figure. Round to the nearest tenth, if necessary.**

a.

Area of Parallelogram    Area of Triangle
$A = bh$      $A = \frac{1}{2}bh$
$A = 7(7.5)$ or 52.5    $A = \frac{1}{2}(15 \cdot 7.5)$
                 $A = 56.25$

The area of the figure is $52.5 + 56.25$ or about 108.8 m².

b.

Area of Semicircle    Area of Triangle
$A = \frac{1}{2}\pi r^2$      $A = \frac{1}{2}bh$
$A = \frac{1}{2}\pi(4.5)^2$    $A = \frac{1}{2}(9 \cdot 13)$
$A = 31.8$          $A = 58.5$

The area of the figure is $31.8 + 58.5$ or about 90.3 yd².

**Exercises**

**Find the area of each figure. Round to the nearest tenth, if necessary.**

1. What is the area of a figure formed using a rectangle with a base of 10 yards and a height of 4 yards and two semicircles, one with a radius of 5 yards and the other a radius of 2 yards? 85.6 yd²

2. Find the area of a figure formed using a square and three triangles all with sides of 9 centimeters. Each triangle has a height of 6 centimeters. 162 cm²

**Find the area of each shaded region. Round to the nearest tenth. (Hint: Find the total area and subtract the non-shaded area.)**

3. 6.9 cm²

4. 110.8 in²

5. 169 m²

Chapter 10    50    Glencoe Pre-Algebra

NAME ________________ DATE __________ PERIOD ____

# 10-8 Practice
## Area: Composite Figures

**Find the area of each figure to the nearest tenth, if necessary.**

1. 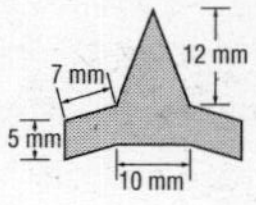


180 mm²

2. 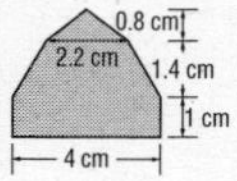


9.2 cm²

3. 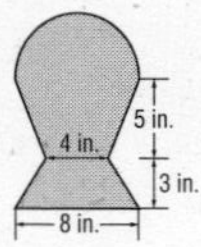


73.1 in²

4. 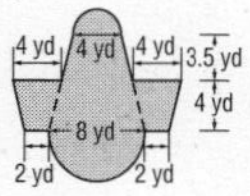


100.4 yd²

5. 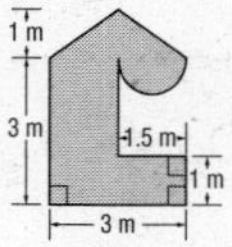


8.4 m²

6. 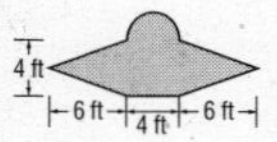


46.3 ft²

7. 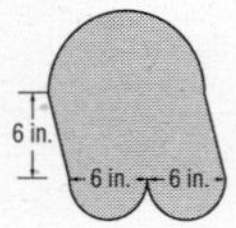


156.8 in²

8. 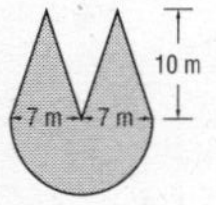


147.0 m²

9. What is the area of a figure formed using a square with sides of 15 centimeters and four attached semicircles? **578.4 cm²**

10. Find the area of a figure formed using a parallelogram with a base of 10 yards and a height of 12 yards and two triangles with bases of 10 yards and heights of 5 yards. **170 yd²**

**Find the area of each shaded area. Round to the nearest tenth, if necessary. (*Hint:* Find the total area and subtract the non-shaded area.)**

11. 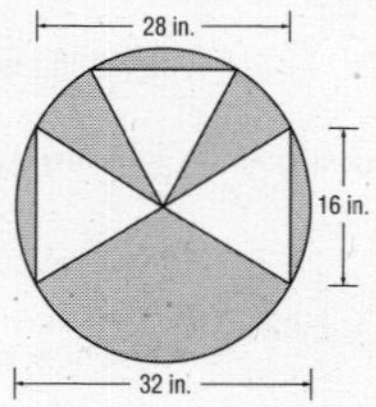


468.2 in²

12. 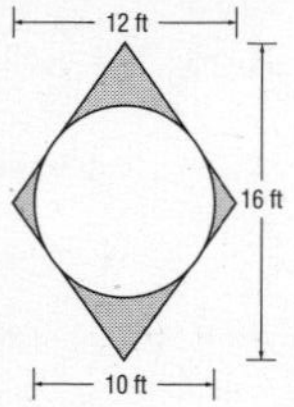


17.5 ft²

13. 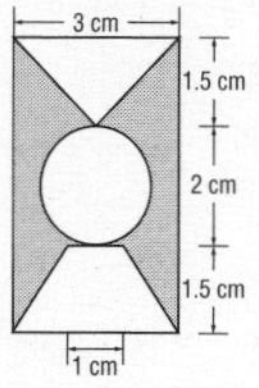


6.6 cm²

14. **HISTORY** What is the area of the track in the Circus Maximus as represented below? The center barrier was named the *spina*. **48,307.9 yd²**

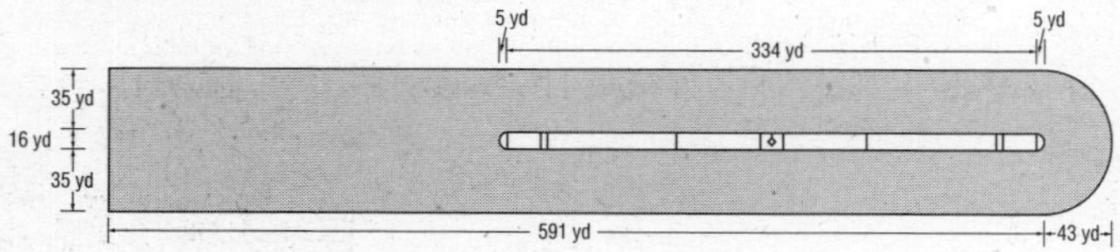






NAME ________________ DATE __________ PERIOD ____

# 10-8 Word Problem Practice
## Area: Composite Figures

1. **SHELVING** The back of a shelving unit is shown below. How much plywood is needed to construct this piece of the unit? Round to the nearest whole number.

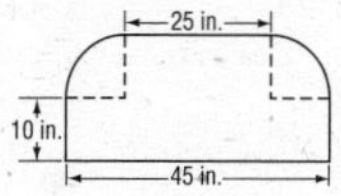


857 in²

2. **LANDSCAPING** Peter's backyard is rectangular in shape, with dimensions 60 feet by 50 feet. He plans to install a circular above ground pool that has a diameter of 20 feet. What will be the area of his backyard that is left after installing the pool? Round to the nearest whole number. **2686 ft²**

3. **DOG HOUSES** Barbara is going to paint the front of her dog's house green. If one quart of paint covers 8 square feet, will she need more than one quart?

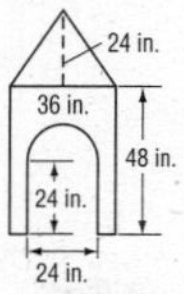


**Yes; the area of front is 9.43 ft².**

4. **LOGOS** The logo for Super Soda Company is shown below. What is the area of the shaded region?

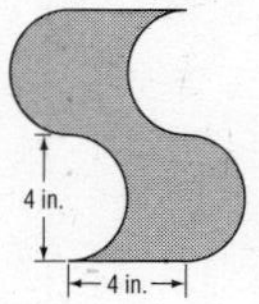


32 in.²

**BOATS For Exercises 5 and 6, use the following information.**

Frank is using a template to make a boat cover out of canvas for his boat. The template is shown below.

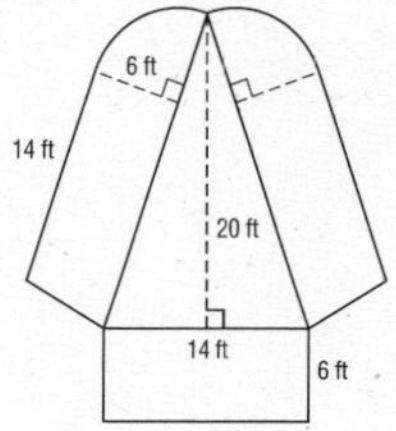


5. How many square feet of canvas will he need to make the template? **448.5 ft²**

6. If canvas costs $8.00 a square yard, how much will the canvas cost? **$398.67**

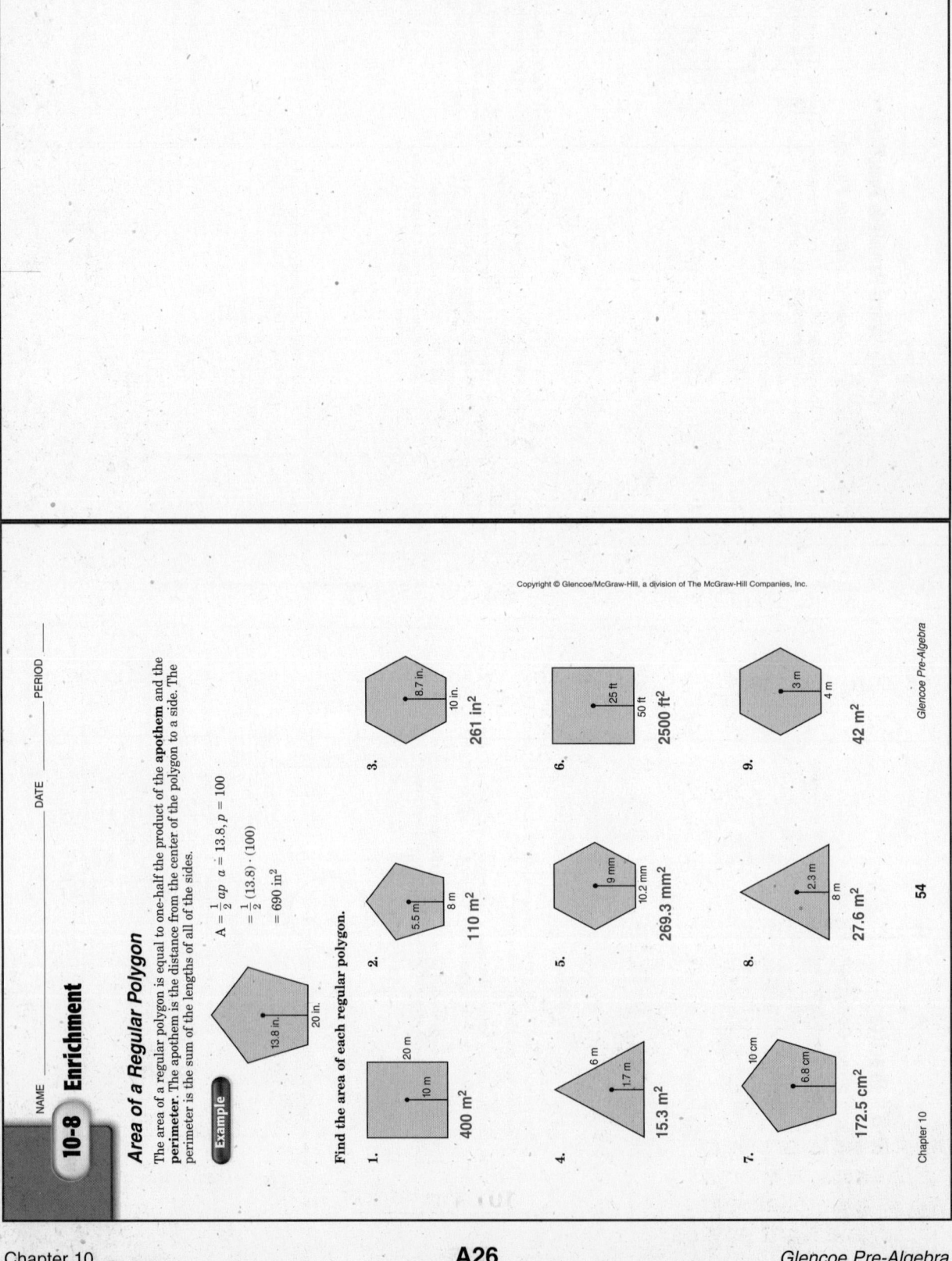

## Area of a Regular Polygon

The area of a regular polygon is equal to one-half the product of the **apothem** and the **perimeter**. The apothem is the distance from the center of the polygon to a side. The perimeter is the sum of the lengths of all of the sides.

**Example**

$A = \frac{1}{2}ap$    $a = 13.8, p = 100$

$\phantom{A} = \frac{1}{2}(13.8) \cdot (100)$

$\phantom{A} = 690 \text{ in}^2$

13.8 in.

20 in.

**Find the area of each regular polygon.**

1.
20 m
10 m
**400 m²**

2.
5.5 m
8 m
**110 m²**

3.
8.7 in.
10 in.
**261 in²**

4.
6 m
1.7 m
**15.3 m²**

5.
9 mm
10.2 mm
**269.3 mm²**

6.
25 ft
50 ft
**2500 ft²**

7.
10 cm
6.8 cm
**172.5 cm²**

8.
2.3 m
8 m
**27.6 m²**

9.
3 m
4 m
**42 m²**

# Chapter 10 Assessment Answer Key

**Quiz 1** (Lessons 10-1 and 10-2)
**Page 57**

1. _____85°_____

2. _____95°_____

3. _____95°_____

4. _____B_____

5. _____$\overline{ZW}$_____

**Quiz 2** (Lessons 10-3 and 10-4)
**Page 57**

1. ___$A'(0, -3)$, $B'(3, -4)$,___
   ___$C'(1, -1)$, $D'(3, -2)$___

2. _____rotation_____

3. _____120°_____

4. _____trapezoid_____

5. **Sample answer: Tennis; the court is a parallelogram with 4 right angles.**

**Quiz 3** (Lessons 10-5 and 10-6)
**Page 58**

1. _____$96 \text{ cm}^2$_____

2. _____$9 \text{ ft}^2$_____

3. _____$17.4 \text{ m}^2$_____

4. _____6_____

5. _____108°_____

**Quiz 4** (Lessons 10-7 and 10-8)
**Page 58**

1. ___$25.1 \text{ m}$; $50.3 \text{ m}^2$___

2. ___$33.0 \text{ ft}$; $86.6 \text{ ft}^2$___

3. ___$4.4 \text{ ft}$; $1.5 \text{ ft}^2$___

4. _____$24 \text{ cm}^2$_____

5. _____$101.4 \text{ m}^2$_____

**Mid-Chapter Test**
**Page 59**

1. ___C___

2. ___F___

3. ___A___

4. ___G___

5. ___D___

6. _____135°_____

7.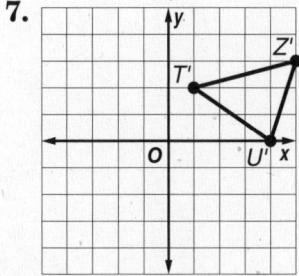

8. _____trapezoid_____

9. _____60_____

10. ___60°, 60°, 120°___

# Chapter 10 Assessment Answer Key

**Vocabulary Test**
**Page 60**

1. circumference

2. congruent

3. diameter

4. perpendicular lines

5. polygon

6. quadrilateral

7. reflection

8. supplementary angles

9. translation

10. vertical angles

11. a line that interesects two other lines

12. the ratio of the circumference of a circle to the diameter of a circle

**Form 1**
**Page 61**

1. C

2. G

3. C

4. H

5. A

6. F

7. C

8. H

9. C

10. J

11. B

**Page 62**

12. F

13. A

14. H

15. C

16. F

17. C

18. G

19. C

20. J

B: 18 in.

# Chapter 10 Assessment Answer Key

**Form 2A**
**Page 63**

**Page 64**

**Form 2B**
**Page 65**

**Page 66**

1. A
2. H
3. B
4. G
5. D
6. F
7. B
8. H
9. A
10. H

11. A
12. H
13. A
14. J
15. B
16. G
17. D
18. J
19. B
20. J
B: _____9:1_____

1. B
2. F
3. C
4. J
5. B
6. F
7. A
8. H
9. C
10. G

11. D
12. H
13. C
14. G
15. A
16. J
17. D
18. H
19. B
20. G
B: _____30 in²_____

Answers

# Chapter 10 Assessment Answer Key

**Form 2C**
**Page 67**

Page 68

1. _____ 102° _____

2. _____ 78° _____

3. _____ 52° _____

4. _____ 65° _____

5. _____ $\overline{BC}$ _____

14. _____ 32.4 in. _____

15. _____ 540° _____

16. _____ 156° _____

17. _____ 20.42 cm _____

18. _____ 49.01 in. _____

19. _____ 62.83 cm _____

20. _____ 94.25 ft _____

6. _____ 12 cm _____

7.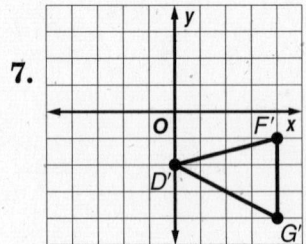

8.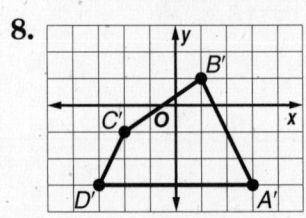

9. _____ 17.9 in² _____

10. _____ 46.2 m² _____

11. _____ 380.1 cm² _____

12. _____ 72; 72°, 144° _____

13. _____ rhombus _____

21. _____ 88.1 in² _____

22. _____ 59.9 cm² _____

23. _____ 36.3 cm² _____

24. _____ 63.4 in² _____

25. _____ 6 m _____

B: _____ about 24.25 mm _____

# Chapter 10 Assessment Answer Key

**Form 2D**
**Page 69**

1. _____ 138° _____

2. _____ 42° _____

3. _____ 168° _____

4. _____ 87° _____

5. _____ $\overline{YZ}$ _____

6. _____ 11 cm _____

7.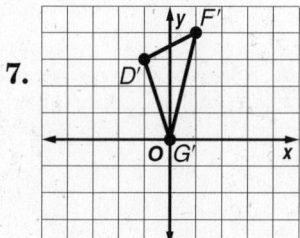

8. 

9. _____ 28.1 ft² _____

10. _____ 54.6 m² _____

11. _____ 452.4 cm² _____

12. _____ 60; 60°, 120° _____

13. _____ rectangle _____

**Page 70**

14. _____ 37.8 cm _____

15. _____ 720° _____

16. _____ 157.5° _____

17. _____ 39.27 cm _____

18. _____ 30.79 in. _____

19. _____ 81.68 cm _____

20. _____ 78.54 ft _____

21. _____ 47.6 in² _____

22. _____ 46.6 cm² _____

23. _____ 58.1 cm² _____

24. _____ 24.9 cm² _____

25. _____ 7 m _____

B: _____ 83.3 mm _____

Answers

# Chapter 10 Assessment Answer Key

1. _____18_____

2. _____7_____

3. _____70°_____

4. _____EAD_____

5. _____8_____

6.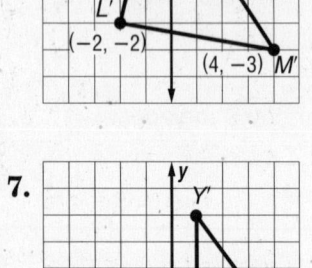

7.

8. _____70_____

9. Sometimes; a square is a rhombus and a rectangle.

10. _____43.7 cm²_____

11. _____18.4 in²_____

12. _____46.5 m²_____

13. _____54.8 ft²_____

14. _____12-gon; regular_____

15. _____3420°_____

16. _____168°_____

17. _____9.7 in._____

18. _____8.0 cm_____

19. _____776_____

20. _____92 units²_____

B: _____$A = h^2$_____

# Chapter 10 Assessment Answer Key

## Page 73, Extended-Response Test
## Scoring Rubric

| Score | General Description | Specific Criteria |
|-------|---------------------|-------------------|
| 4 | **Superior** A correct solution that is supported by well-developed, accurate explanations | • Shows thorough understanding of the concepts of *relationships of intersecting lines, complementary and supplementary angles, transformations, congruence, areas,* and *angle measures of polygons.* <br>• Uses appropriate strategies to solve problems. <br>• Computations are correct. <br>• Written explanations are exemplary. <br>• Drawings are accurate and appropriate. <br>• Goes beyond requirements of some or all problems. |
| 3 | **Satisfactory** A generally correct solution, but may contain minor flaws in reasoning or computation | • Shows an understanding of the concepts of *relationships of intersecting lines, complementary and supplementary angles, transformations, congruence, areas,* and *angle measures of polygons.* <br>• Uses appropriate strategies to solve problems. <br>• Computations are mostly correct. <br>• Written explanations are effective. <br>• Drawings are mostly accurate and appropriate. <br>• Satisfies all requirements of problems. |
| 2 | **Nearly Satisfactory** A partially correct interpretation and/or solution to the problem | • Shows an understanding of most of the concepts of *relationships of intersecting lines, complementary and supplementary angles, transformations, congruence, areas,* and *angle measures of polygons.* <br>• May not use appropriate strategies to solve problems. <br>• Computations are mostly correct. <br>• Written explanations are satisfactory. <br>• Drawings are mostly accurate. <br>• Satisfies the requirements of most of the problems. |
| 1 | **Nearly Unsatisfactory** A correct solution with no supporting evidence or explanation | • Final computation is correct. <br>• No written explanations or work is shown to substantiate the final computation. <br>• Drawings may be accurate but lack detail or explanation. <br>• Satisfies minimal requirements of some of the problems. |
| 0 | **Unsatisfactory** An incorrect solution indicating no mathematical understanding of the concept or task, or no solution is given | • Shows little or no understanding of most of the concepts of *relationships of intersecting lines, complementary and supplementary angles, transformations, congruence, areas,* and *angle measures of polygons.* <br>• Does not use appropriate strategies to solve problems. <br>• Computations are incorrect. <br>• Written explanations are unsatisfactory. <br>• Drawings are inaccurate or inappropriate. <br>• Does not satisfy requirements of problems. <br>• No answer may be given. |

# Chapter 10 Assessment Answer Key

## Page 73, Extended-Response Test
## Sample Answers

*In addition to the scoring rubric found on page A33, the following sample answers may be used as guidance in evaluating open-ended assessment items.*

**1a.** translation; Each of the *x*-coordinates of △*ABC* is translated 3 units to the right. The *y*-coordinates remain the same.

**1b.** yes; The lengths of the sides of both triangles are 2, 3, and $\sqrt{13}$ respectively. The respective angles also appear to have the same measures. Moving the triangle to the right did not change the size or shape of the triangle.

**1c.** You could draw a picture of a child on a swing on a coordinate grid. You could then transform this picture by keeping the top of the screen the same and drawing the swing at a different angle, thus making a rotation.

**1d.**

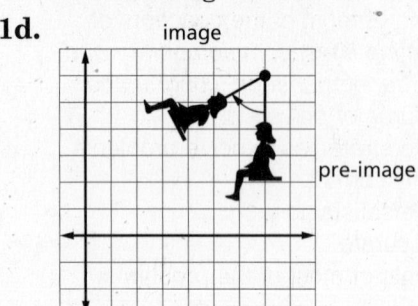

**2a.** Sample answer: ∠*CBA* and ∠*CBA'*; They are formed by two intersecting lines and they are adjacent.

**2b.** Sample answer: ∠*B* and ∠*C*; ∠*A* is a right angle because it is formed by the *x*- and *y*-axes. △*ABC* is a right triangle.

$m\angle A + m\angle B + m\angle C = 180°$
$90° + m\angle B + m\angle C = 180°$
$90° + m\angle B + m\angle C - 90° = 180° - 90°$
$m\angle B + m\angle C = 90°$

**2c.** Sample answer: ∠*CAD* and ∠*B'AE*; They are formed by intersecting lines.

**2d.** Sample answer: The *x*- and *y*-axes are perpendicular.

**3.** Check students' work. The figure should contain the following parts: triangle, trapezoid, parallelogram, and circle. Students should have all bases and altitudes correctly identified. Students may rely on the definitions of parallelogram to imply equal sides. Look for symbols that indicate parallel lines and perpendicular lines.

**4a.** the sum of the measures

**4b.** The sum of the measures of all the interior angles of any polygon can be found using the formula $(n - 2)180$. For regular polygons, all of the interior angles have the same measure. So the total can be divided by the number of sides to find the measure of each angle. For a non-regular polygon, there are an unlimited number of possibilities for the measures of each interior angle.

## Standardized Test Practice

**Page 74**

1. A B ● D
2. F G H ●
3. A ● C D
4. ● G H J
5. A ● C D
6. ● G H J
7. A B ● D
8. F G ● J
9. A B C ●
10. F ● H J

**Page 75**

11. ● B C D
12. ● G H J
13. A ● C D
14. F G ● J
15. A B ● D
16. F G ● J
17. A B ● D

18. 3 8 4 .

19. 6 8 4 0 .

# Chapter 10 Assessment Answer Key

## Standardized Test Practice

**Page 76**

20. _____ 32 _____

21. _____ $0.1\overline{6}$ _____

22. _____ false _____

23. _____ $y = x + 5$ _____

24. _____ 15.6 _____

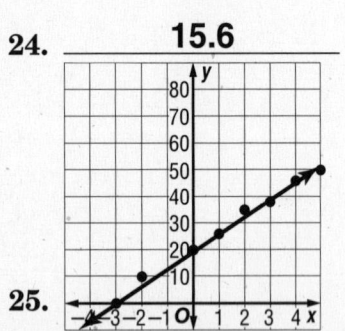

25.

26. sample answer: 15

27. _____ 155° _____

28. _____ 180 cm² _____

29. _____ 8640° _____

30a. _____ $72 = 0.3x + 24$ _____

30b. _____ 160 _____

30c. _____ yes _____